Farmer's Diary

Charlie Allan

Illustrations by
Turnbull

Ardo Publishing Company
Methlick, Aberdeenshire AB41 0HR

FS|ALL·
789982

I am grateful to the *Herald* for permission
to reproduce these articles, which first appeared
in print in that newspaper.

Published by Ardo Publishing Company, Buchan

Printed in Great Britain by BPC Wheaton Ltd, Exeter

Foreword

I SAID at the beginning of Volume Three that I was on a treadmill. When we brought out Volume Two there was a wee rush on Volume One. We were left with so many Volume Twos that we brought out Volume Three to see if it would help shift Volume Two. It did, so Volume Four was needed to sell Vols Two and Three.

And when we ran out of Volume One a few said they didn't want to start with Volume Three. They would not buy any unless they could start at the beginning so we had to have a second impression of the first book.

And the treadmill is worse than that even. As I write, I am well on with writing the stuff that would appear in Volume Five. I will not be able to resist publishing it if I have it written so I will need a Volume Six to help the sale of Five.

I tell you the life of a farmer who writes it down is not easy. Will I ever be able to retire?

I suppose, if Jim Turnbull were to retire that would put a stop to it. The books would not be the same without him and I am indebted to him once again for permission to reproduce his cartoons.

The Breadwinner has done the desk-top publishing again. She has retired now from earning the money my farming denied us, so she has become a full-time publisher as well as being able to keep her husband under constant surveillance.

Sarah Purdie read the proofs and spied all sorts of things I had overlooked or had thought were correct.

The only other help I had was from Messrs AppleMac in the shape of a computerised speller. You may be annoyed to find a few remaining spelling "mistakes". They may not be real mistakes. You see Mr Macintosh is an American and he keeps telling me to change things to the correct (American) spelling.

Murray Webster and the printers at BCP Wheatons made a good job of Volume Three. If they have kept up the good work with Volume Four we will be very grateful and consider them for the printing of Volume Five.

3

This volume is dedicated to William Yull, John Yull, Maitland Mackie and John Allan, the ancestors in whose steps I run here on Ardo's hill.

The story so far

ONE OF Charlie Allan's eight great-great-grandfathers, all of whom were farmers so far as is known, had two daughters due to be married at the same time. In a piece of generosity and chauvinism of heroic proportions the old man offered the fine farm of Skillmafilly to the first grandson to be produced by either union.

As an indirect consequence of his great grandmother winning the contest, the author's grandfather became the farmer of North Ythsie farm in Tarves. And that was Charlie's point of entry into the farming community of the North-east of Scotland.

For, despite that family background on the land, the author was born to parents both of whom were away from the soil earning a frugal living by their pens. John R. Allan was a freelance journalist who earned five pounds in one astonishingly good week and his wife twice had an article in the Pick of Punch. The move from honest literary poverty, to the home of a gentleman farmer in Aberdeenshire was all the doing of Adolf Hitler. He diverted both parents from writing and their son, to the war effort. Charlie was put to stay with his granny and grandpa on North Ythsie farm. There cannot be many who have so much for which to thank Hitler.

People used to talk of having had a good war. Well, for Charlie it was magic. He seemed to have his grandparents all to himself, as well as their huge farmhouse and garden. In addition he had a succession of young airmen from the Empire who gave him the affection due to the brothers and sisters they had left behind in Australia, Canada or South Africa.

A farm was found for the conquering hero after the war. It was not as grand a place as North Ythsie but Little Ardo had been broken in by another great-great-grandfather, William Yull, so the weight of his ancestors was born down on the boy from that tender age.

The boy was able to buy Little Ardo from his parents in 1976 for half the market value or twice what it was worth, whichever way you prefer to look at it.

For the next ten years an attempt to pay the bank their

interest was made under the theory that if a hundred cows on the farm would produce £x then a thousand cattle would produce £10x. It is the theory the college used to advise. After every new disaster they proposed that farmers find room for another ten cows.

By 1986, Charlie was exhausted and the overdraft was worse than ever, so the opposite policy was tried. That worked. When the seven hundred cattle were reduced to one hundred the overdraft disappeared and profits appeared.

This called for a holiday. Charlie would go to Kenya for a break and he would depend on his wife Fiona to be the Breadwinner. This she did for three years while he, without complaint, did nothing in particular, but with aplomb.

These diaries started when he returned from Kenya and restarted farming Little Ardo from scratch. Each volume covers about fourteen months and Volume Four starts at the end of June 1993. It covers that dreary summer when Mossie managed to grow sunflowers despite the fact that there were only four days of sunshine during the growing season. That year they finished the harvest in early November.

By contrast there was the summer and harvest of 1994 where there were some record crops despite the drought, and Charlie became the first man in Scotland to sell a heifer with a passport. The CCDs, as they are called, are supposed to be carried only by steers.

Charlie and Fiona Allan have been married for 35 years and have four children and five grandchildren. Volume Four covers the decision on retirement and on the succession to the family acres.

June 23, 1993

Judge in jeans and trainers

As they stepped into the ring I used to think the judges had an awful majesty. They came from a distance. They were so famous you could sometimes read their names in the paper. And on that day when the best in the country had been gathered together, they were the arbiters of judgement. Although they were quite ordinary bodies, they took on a remote, impartial air for the occasion. During the next two hours their word was law, beyond all question.

THUS MY father wrote about the show in his diary forty-one years ago. And when I lean against the rail, watching the judging at this year's Royal Highland Show, I'll remember it well. And I'll also remember the great (for me) occasion when I first judged at a show overseas.

It was no tuppenny ha'penny affair either, but the great Nairobi International Show, an event lasting most of a week and welcoming a quarter of a million visitors.

Now you might think that I would be nervous about a contract like that and you'd be right. But I told myself what I have told many another since, that an expert is just some fool a hundred miles from home. As I was seven thousand miles

from home I was surely an expert judge of cattle many times over. Besides, the natural good manners of the Kenyans meant that even if I got it wrong there was absolutely no chance of them telling me.

I decided that, as it was an international show, I would wear the kilt even though Nairobi is on the equator and the show was likely to be held at 30 degrees centigrade. I worked over in my mind little points like the importance of good walking for cattle who would have to range for many miles in search of their daily grass. And I made up my mind not to be tempted to show how quickly I could line them up but to take a good while over every decision to give the losers the consolation that it was a close

7

one.

I was all set for my big day on the second day of the show but decided I would sneak along on the opening day, just to see what it would be like. I put on the dark glasses, jeans and trainers. Judges are not supposed to see the cattle before they are presented in the ring, but I thought I'd like to get just a sighter.

Thank goodness I went. No sooner had I snuck into the ground when my daughter came running up, "Dad, for goodness sake. They've been calling for you for ages. You're supposed to be judging the Belgian Blues."

And so it was that I made my international debut late, out of breath, without kilt, without dignity and without even a clean pair of shoes.

So much for the 'awe inspiring majesty' of the judges. And what about 'the best in the country being gathered together' to watch the judges in action? Well, in Nairobi my audience included a sizeable group of the most dedicated cattlemen in the world: the famous and feared Maasai tribesmen.

Now Kenya has a sophisticated population which I see making so many of the mistakes of modernism that we have made here in the past.

They are keen to sweep away the old and embrace all the brashness of the modern West. That applies to the Kenyan authorities and to the Kenyan people - except the Maasai.

The government is having the greatest difficulty in persuading the Maasai to give up their traditional ways and join the modern state. But they have their traditional ways and they are sticking very well to them. And those traditions are based on the cow.

The cow provides their food - all of it. Nothing but milk, blood and beef. Cow skins provide bedding and cow dung is used to make the walls of their houses. Cows are a man's wealth. Where a farmer in Scotland might sell his cows for money, a Maasai has no use for money except to buy more cows. If a dowry is asked, cows are the currency. The only work a Maasai does is cow-herding when he is young, and cultural pursuits like dancing, worship and warfare.

The Maasai believe that God gave all cows to them. Traditionally they believe that if someone else is seen with cows then they must have stolen them.

So here was I presuming to judge cows before the most dedicated cowmen of all.

What the Maasai thought

8

of my judging, I do not know. There was not a clue on their faces. They stood absolutely still without talking, until, just as I was making my final flourish to indicate my Supreme Champion, they all glided off, without a word or a sign.

For me, the serious business of this year's Highland will be what happens in the judging ring though I know that is only the stuff of make-believe.

The real work is in the machinery lines and there I intend to do better than last year. Then I set out to get myself a handle that would allow me to put off my sprayer without the agonising stretch round at the start and finish of each pass. Unfortunately, I accepted Mossie's offer to negotiate the purchase.

He did a wonderful deal. I was promised thirty percent off. But it was too good a deal for the handle never arrived and my side is again black and blue where I bash it on the tractor seat as I dive for the handle at the end of each row. This year I'm going to the machinery boys alone and I'll pay their price.

If machinery is not the main stuff of the show then perhaps conviviality is. Things have not changed much. My father's diary about the show in 1952 records it winding down for another year:

Then it was time for the wives to collect their husbands and go home; and soon it was time to go home without them.

9

Old Fergie comes to the rescue

I TELL myself often how lucky I am to sit here, a bonnet laird and clear of the banker, with wide views over rural Aberdeenshire to the South and with a bit of shelter from the wind that sometimes howls down from the North.

But I don't like to tell myself that too often. There is a force which looks after the lives of farmers who become complacent. And that force was active this week.

After telling you last week how much I was enjoying working my sprayer, I might have known He would do a bit of evening up.

I just have Mossie's secret brew to apply to the spring rape and a headspray to the wheat and I'll be finished. A bounteous harvest beckons. Last Wednesday I loaded the brew into the sprayer and set off for the field. Before I got started the rain came on - lashing down out of a blue sky.

Now, not only can you not spray to any effect in the rain, but you can't switch off and go and watch the test match. If you do that, the whole thing congeals and you are left with a thousand gallons of expensive poison, the consistency of jelly, that turns quickly to chalk. All the pipes of the sprayer seize up and the machinery salesmen start to circle.

The consultant said it would be alright if I kept the machine going and mixing away until the weather dried up.

I lay all night listening to the poor old Fergie grinding away. Would she heat and leave me looking for a new tractor *and* a new sprayer? All next day it rained or nearly stopped. Mossie took a friendly interest. "Is that brew nae mixed yet?" and, "Have you ordered mair diesel for your tractor?"

On Friday there was a blink in the weather in the late afternoon. I added a pint of Bond, which cuts the time the leaves have to stay dry to as little as ten minutes. In great relief I set out for the field. I could see that the rain would not be on for at least half an hour. I would at least have time to do the first field.

Or I would have had. I was reversing into the field when there was a crack from the front of my tractor and the left track-rod end fell off. That means that only one wheel turns when you move the steering-wheel.

I once did a quarter mile in fifty-four seconds so it should not have taken me long to run back to the steading. It took a bit longer on Friday though I arrived there just as out of breath. Luckily I was able to get hold of an old inner tube, cut off three slices and hobble back to the field.

In quite a lot of time I had the track-rod end back in place, tied with wire and twisted round with inner tube. Finally I was ready to start spraying.

I started even though it was just beginning to spit, but by the time I had gone right round it was bucketing down again. I would have been back at square one if it hadn't been that I now had Bond, a renowned sticker, added to the cocktail.

On Friday the poor old Fergie had to work through the night at double speed to try to keep it mixing. Saturday dawned fair and stayed fair. I got my field done but what with I really don't know. Most of the chemicals were in a solid lump, about three inches deep, in the bottom of the sprayer. Still, at least I had got rid of the liquid.

It took me the rest of Saturday and all day Sunday to get the tank clear and the jets unblocked.

Mossie was encouraging though. He told me I would get blockages every few yards for the rest of the season.

11

It's not all bad news. You will remember that I bought thirteen old bangers to make my cow numbers up and qualify me for quota under the new Common Market rules. Those cost an average of three hundred a-piece, being bought at the cheaper end of the market.

Well, we've had two deaths and three calves and the prices have at least doubled. We had put the old dears in with Argus, the Simmental bull, because we had been told that, even though the intention was to replace them with the Black Hereford heifers, we had to make a serious attempt to breed them.

I was looking forward to putting the last eight to the jingoring and doubling my money but we thought we should have the vet check them. Though Argus had not been seen taking any interest, all eight are seven months in calf. I am to have an autumn calving, and who knows, if they have bull calves, I may yet treble my money.

At the very least Argus deserves a half pailful of best dairy cake.

It is a triumph but it is nothing to Mossie's sunflowers which the crazy EC are paying him a king's ransom to grow in the moss.

With no prospect of a harvest, our man is making the best of all the blawing opportunities meantime. They are really looking remarkably well, healthy plants and plenty of room to spread, but he is meeting with a good deal of scepticism.

And yet he's not good to beat. I heard him telling a group the other day at the debriefing after the annual Meldrum Sports that his Happy Faces were now three feet six high. Unfortunately, there was a reveller in the crowd who had seen them and insisted that they were only six inches.

Mossie can be cornered but never beaten. "Oh aye, that maybe, but you dinna ken how deep I planted them," he said. Anyway, they're all sold on contract. The florist has agreed to take any that get as far as flowering.

July 5, 1993

Jaguar status symbol has a day out

I KNOW Ian Grant has come a long way since he was only the President of the National Farmers' Union of Scotland. He's big in a bank and a colossus in the Tourist Board for a start, but I did think he was a bit off-hand when I met him at the Highland.

He has always been an affable chap and so, when I saw him taking a keen interest in the judging of the inter-breed cattle championships, I bounced in about for a chat.

I have to say that I became quickly aware that I was more interested in the chat than he was. He was no more than polite with my important remarks and a weak smile was all I could get for even my best jokes.

Well, I've seen it before. Success is not easy for some people to take, especially when they're not used to it.

And every now and again, he would fix his eyes on the middle distance and start rambling on about this team of

Simmentals having too small a bull, the Salers all being too high at the tail or the Murray Greys being too wee. When he did that, I fairly thought the beginning of the end was in sight for the man who had once been the rising star of Scottish farming.

I needn't have worried as it turns out. You see he was working. He'd been employed by the BBC to burst forth into learned commentary every now and again. If you watch Landward on Sunday you may see me. I'm the guy on Ian's right. The one who is always trying to speak to him and looks as though he's just trying to get into the picture.

I had a really good show though I only got down for the one day. You see the Breadwinner relented and let me take the Jaguar down to Edinburgh.

She's never forgiven me for buying it when I got fou at Smithfield. She's not interested that it was only a third of the new price at two years old, nor

13

that it was without a blemish. "It's just not you." she says.

That wouldn't be so hurtful if I didn't know what she thinks is appropriate for me. She has never refused to go in my old diesel Cavalier, at least after I have mucked it out.

So it was a breakthrough when she agreed we would take the Jag to the Highland. But what if no-one saw us arriving? What a blow if all I could do was wave my car keys around absent-mindedly. Never mind it would be a good run down and the Jaggie would be the better of it.

She has lain in the tattie a power washer.

As we swished South I noticed that my beautiful metallic-blue status symbol handled oddly when we passed petrol stations. When you drive a diesel Cavalier and feed it out of the farm tank you forget about these things, but the Jaggie gets quite nervous at the approach of a filling station. At first it was just that she seemed to lose a bit of power. But it got worse and worse until she was pulling hard to the left every time we neared a pump. At Perth I gave up when she started missing, pulled to the left and started signalling.

shed for the last few months and right under the flight path of a nest of starlings, so there was a fair washing to be done. That settled it. If I got nothing else at the Highland it would be

I withdrew the pump at £40 worth. I just couldn't stand it any more. You know, that is almost twice what I paid for my first car and forty times what I got when I sold her. Still it would get me to Edinburgh and that was the job in hand.

The judging was done by Drew Adam of Newhouse of Glamis where he carries on the great family traditions of cattle breeding. There were three fewer breeds than the last time I saw the competition. That led me to think about who was missing: the Welsh Blacks, the Red Devons and the Romagnolas, I thought.

And that reminded me of the judge's father, the great Bob Adam, and the time that the Chianinas were imported from Italy.

They are the tallest cattle in the world and the Americans wanted them - badly. They sent agents over who paid up to £25,000 for these gangly brutes which "killed out like cricket bats" according to a butcher from Aberdeen.

Anyway, for some reason there was an extra heifer in the importation and it was between a few of us who would get it and who would have to take bulls which were not expected to be worth the asking price. Eventually there was a draw and who should win it but Bob Adam.

Now that was some raffle, because the tickets were costing £2,900 and the lucky winner's prize was worth at least £10,000. None of the participants was less in need of the money than Bob but of course his name came out of the hat. "Just as it should be," he said.

One of the most spectacular animals at this year's show was an Aberdeen-Angus cow. She was so enormous that she couldn't get into the breed team because she would swamp the bull, but she won the 'Bred by the Exhibitor' class despite being against the reserve champion animal of the whole show.

Now, Drew Adam gave as a very important part of his reasoning behind his choice, the animal's great size. And the interesting thing is how that contrasts with the breeding old Bob did in the hey-day of the export trade.

Bob Adam is said to have told young farmers and anyone else who deserved to learn, that the ideal Black should have a flat top line, a flat bottom line and be as close to the ground as possible.

Of course no-one should criticise Drew for his choice of that monster cow. He is producing for a market, and so was his father. It's just that the market has changed.

15

Euro lunacy for growing hay fever

HARVEST APPROACHES and we are getting excited.

I have told you before that according to Mossie everybody has a four tonne crop when the braird is established. Each mistake after that and each natural disaster, like the eclipse of the sun or floods, reduces the yield so that in the end of the day, the good farmers get nearly four tonnes and the bad ones get nearly two tonnes - but tell you in the pub it was nearly three.

Well now, the exciting thing is that we have made few mistakes despite trying quite hard and there has been no natural disaster. Things are looking well.

There is a bit of scorch in the wheat from the Twerpall, but I'm told that is nothing to worry about. The winter barley is also scorched, though no-one knows what with, but that crop is here already so there doesn't seem to be much likely to go wrong with it.

16

But the real star turn is the winter rape. It is a notoriously difficult crop to guestimate but it is looking much better than anything I've grown before.

All round Aberdeenshire you can see crops of rape looking heavy, too heavy in fact, for they are flat. But, on the advice of the great cerealiser, I have sown a blend of two rapes. I did ask his permission to tell you the secret and he said, "Oh aye. It used to be 'closed shop' stuff. I've been daein it for eight years but aabody's daein it noo, so I suppose you can tell them."

It must indeed be old hat but, just in case you didn't know, here is the secret of our blending.

First, there is Falcon which seems to be the heaviest yielding crop around here. It's the variety I saw at Mossie's two years ago and refused to believe that it was rape and not some sort of giant forage peas. My Falcon is looking very well, though nothing like as good as Mossie's was two years ago. If I can keep it green, it will fill and fill my cart as never before.

But the bonus is that if you look down among the stems of the Falcon you will see a short and strong variety called Samourai which is also looking well. Where the pods of the Falcon stop, look for the pods of the Samourai. That gives me three foot six of pods instead of two feet at most without the blend. And the short Samourai holds the gangling Falcon up to the light and to the breeze, so that it can go on filling well into August.

I have to admit that there is a down side. I am growing as many weeds as spring rape. I'll be disappointed if I don't get well over a tonne and a half of winter rape but, if someone would offer me a tonne for this year's spring rape crop, I'd fairly take it.

Mind you, with the Euro-lunacy at its height for rape, the yield of the spring stuff hardly matters. I've just had Mossie on the phone with the news that the subsidy for growing hay fever is to be £204 an acre. That could be a tonne and a half for a start, and no combining or drying charges.

He tells me that set-aside is to be £97 and for that you don't even have to sow it. And they're giving us £54 an acre for growing barley and wheat.

Now that cereal subsidy has Mossie fair mad at the unfairness of it. "£54 an acre is eighteen pounds a tonne to you, noo that I've got ye a kinda sorted oot. Them that canna fairm are gettin twenty-seven pounds a tonne. But a boy like me, growin nearly five tonnes, I'm only getting eleven pounds a tonne.

It's jist nae fair."

In fact Mossie's really quite frustrated just now, and it's not just the calm before the storm of harvest, when all the blawing comes home to roost.

You see he has just replaced all his sows, and gone through all the hoops necessary to get 'high health' status for his pigs. The new gilts have started farrowing and the little piggies are growing like dollar mushrooms. If you ask him how his pigs are doing all he can say is, "Oh, they're a show. They're a show."

And indeed they may be, but what use is a 'show' to a high health pig man? The one thing you cannot do with high health pigs is show them to anyone. Mossie is finding that it is no use just blawing about your pigs and saying "Sorry but I'm nae allowed to let you see them." The thing about blawing is that there is no pride in it unless there is a risk that you might be found out. Otherwise, you can say what you like, and no one will believe you anyway.

And we don't.

My livestock are doing alright though, and anyone can see them at any time, especially me. In fact, as I write, the cows are a real treat. I have forty-five cows with calves at foot and a bull at their back, in the four-acre paddock in front of the old farmhouse. They make a wonderful show and it is so fine to be able to do the main job of the morning just by drawing back the curtains in the bedroom.

Argus is wearing through his second three-week cycle and it appears that he must have been very active in his first three weeks. Of course, he is a quiet worker, but really there seems to have been very little doing. It is tempting to count each cow as three already.

So all is well on the little farm on the hill. Mind you, I did have a bad moment this week. Mossie phoned and asked me if I had topped the set-aside, as failure to do so could lead to the loss of all those lovely subsidies. I'll have to plead the fifth amendment and refuse to tell you when that was, but it is OK. It is done now.

Flashing blue light leads to trouble

DISASTER HAS struck the discussion group. For years now, we have met at the Salmon Inn on a Sunday to swop ideas on the price of stores, the cheapest source of nitrogen, the poor state that any of our friends who isn't there has let his crops get into, the damnable state of the weather, and the fact that the only thing worse than the present government, would be any other we're likely to get.

The membership stands at about fifteen with a hard core of about half a dozen. It's a sort of Freefarmery. It can be useful if you're needing a spare cart for the mucking, or if your bull goes lame in his busy season. If your combine is free you can pick up a day's work at the discussion group.

And it is a very jolly way to end the week, having a couple of beers with the lads.

But that's where the trouble has come in. Last Sunday, Mains was making his way home from a late session when a car came up behind him and started flashing a blue light. That led to some heavy breathing and the taking of blood samples.

We all await the outcome of the tests with horror. We had no idea that the police even knew where the Salmon was. And it was on a private road that Mains was stopped. We have been trying to get the council to sort that road for years but they insist that it is private and nothing to do with them. But will the courts agree?

I tell you there is more than a mere driving licence resting on this one. Indeed, no less than the whole future of the discussion group is at stake.

If you don't believe it, I can tell you that on Sunday there was only Mains and myself there. He had come by bike, which seemed like a classic case of shutting the door after the shelt had gone. But we agreed that, if the discussion group was to survive, we would all have to take to two wheels. I have a racer left over from my year in the bicycle club ten years ago, and I look forward to seeing Big Hamish rolling up on a racer.

Beside that threat to our way of life, the state of the crops seems secondary at best. I've put the headspray on the wheat, so all I have to do now is wait for harvest. And that wait will be a time of mounting expectation. The barley is starting to turn and all the crops are looking well to my eyes. I still haven't got one blade of the cereals down and the rape isn't even leaning.

Mind you, having your crops standing is not all good. It's a bit like having them ripen first. Just as the poor, underfed and therefore the lightest crops are the first to ripen, so are they the last to bend under the weight of the rains.

I maintain that my barley is standing because we have looked after the disease position so well that the roots are stronger than those of my neighbours. But not everybody sees it that way. Mossie says I'll need to go out and trample a bit of barley near the road before they all start accusing me of having the lightest crops in the county.

And Mossie's had trouble with a snooper. Like me he's got set-aside. But whereas I regard set-aside as an affront to all the hard work my forefathers have done to claim Little Ardo from my moss, Mossie thinks set-aside is a very good idea. It can hardly help paying at £97 an acre for doing nothing much, and it is the ideal

20

break crop, with perfect entry into the most profitable crop of all, wheat.

But it must be a real break. To get maximum advantage, all previous wheats must be killed and it should not be allowed to get too weedy. The obvious thing to do is to spray the set-aside and ensure a perfect break. But that's not allowed unless you get a special dispensation from the Department.

And that's where Mossie was lucky. He was able to tell the Department that he had a terrible outbreak of weeds on the set-aside at Moss-side. There was Wild Oats. There was Sterile Brome. There were Tansies, Scotch Thistles and Skellach, Mayweed, Chickweed, and Giant Hogweed. His dog had disappeared into a thicket of Deadly Black Orchids and had never been seen since.

Thank goodness the Department of Agriculture up here is still the Department of Agriculture. They don't want Aberdeenshire to return to the wilderness. So permission was granted, as a special one-off dispensation, to spray the jungle that was emerging at Moss-side.

That has been done and,

while the rest of us have a variety of weed crops on our set-aside, or lawns which are meant to produce a crop of hay after the fifteenth of July, Mossie has a brown wilderness. It wastes no energy in growing but diligently fixes atmospheric nitrogen against the day in early September when the perfect seed-bed will welcome the wheat bonanza of 1994.

And that's where the snooper came in. He'd been driving along on the snoop when, clearly visible from the back road to Barthol Chapel, there was Mossie's obviously sprayed set-aside. "Allo Allo Allo," said he, and proceeded to the steading where he addressed the farmer in accusatory mode.

"What's this then?"

"That's my set-aside."

The snooper was triumphant. "Well, you can have permanent set-aside or rotational set-aside. And rotational set-aside has to be natural regrowth, bare fallow or green cover crop. So what do you call this?"

"Ah yes," said Mossie, "this is chemical set-aside."

"We'll see about that," said the snooper and left saying, "I'll be back."

We're all hoping he will be - but he's not appeared yet.

21

Knee deep in dubs and sharn

THIS WAS a big year for New Deer Show. And not just because it was the 147th time the New Deer and District Agricultural Society had celebrated the good things about Buchan farming. You see, this was the year of Big Hamish's presidency.

It had been a bad week for the big man as well as a busy one. Not only had Potions the chemist taken his holidays deliberately to avoid helping with the show, but it rained and rained. It wasn't quite as bad as the mid-west of America but on the Thursday night, on the forty-second night of rain in the grain basket of America, Hamish was watching the news on the tele. They showed a map of that fourth Great Lake and how it was growing nightly. Hamish didn't sleep a wink that night for worrying lest it reach New Deer by Saturday.

But the worst didn't happen. The day dawned dull but dry. If the underfoot conditions would hold up, we would get by.

I first saw the big man about eight o'clock. From the knees upward he was looking absolutely splendid in the kilt. Hamish is the right shape for the kilt. But from the knees downward I could clearly see the seeds of trouble.

You could still see that the stockings had started the day off white and even that the brogues had started off black. I advised the wellies but , "Oh na, that widna be smart," said the President. I had to agree though I couldn't see that there was anything very smart about being up to the knees in dubbs and sharn.

Oh, the sacrifices of being President of a local show!

Indeed it wasn't just wet feet that the President had to suffer. Hamish was a 'hands-on' President. Not for him the hiding in the committee tent dishing out drams to those and such as those. No, No. When I arrived on the Friday night with my caravan for the local heritage magazine's stand, it was the President who guided me to my stance.

He even showed me how to

22

set up the caravan. Then he hurried off to place the next stallholder.

Not all of them could drive however. Those of us who have taken country skills in through our pores had a lot of fun watching the new race of country folk, them with the horses and the big fancy four-wheel-drive vehicles, showing that what they really needed was not a pose vehicle but an ordinary driver.

Hamish watched sadly as this man with forty thousand pounds worth of status symbol tried to back his trailer into a space that would have berthed the Queen Mary. The man couldn't have backed a hand cart on level concrete so, on the side of the Den at the end of the first week of the monsoon, he was always going to be strug-gling at New Deer.

But the President backed it in for him and then accepted an earful of abuse for keeping such a wet field.

Next was an amateur float driver who had stuck and thought that his best chance of getting clear was to shout abuse at the President and to tell him to "get your effing act together".

And, funnily enough, that did work.

One thing Hamish can do is act. Now, if you're going to take precipitate action, you are better to be Hamish's size and shape. "Right!" he roared, "get oot o' that". and with one mighty fist grasping the driver by the collar he eased him out and insinuated himself into the driver's seat in one lionine movement. With the lightness of touch of a master musician,

23

the President soon had the lorry out of trouble and up to the loading bay.

Then it was off to sort out a stallholder who had booked a ten-foot frontage but, despite the fact that they were clearly marked, had installed himself in a twenty-footer. No apologies, just more dog's abuse for the President.

And so it went on all day. But it stayed dry and the sun even came out and shone on New Deer and on Big Hamish. The white socks and the ghillies, which at one stage had disappeared altogether, began to reappear as the mud dried and started to flake off.

As I write, it isn't clear whether the 147th show will work out as a success or a triumph. The attendance was certainly among the best ever, record entries in the show sections, a wonderful Grand Parade, outstanding displays in the WRI tent and the prospect of a strengthening balance sheet.

It is all very heartening but who would be a president? Hamish was ready for the dram I gave him at five o'clock and I was glad to be going home. The big man still had the evening programme to get through, bouncing at the dance, the cows to milk in the morning, and then the clearing up which will keep him and his committee from being bored in the next week.

And then they can start worrying about the 148th show.

In the meantime the discussion group is on a high. Mains, as I told you last week, had had a jollier session than usual and had stayed longer than the rest of us at the discussion group. On the way home he had noticed a blue light flashing behind him and had stopped. To his surprise he found that it was the police who invited him to blow in a bag and then to donate some blood at the police station.

This was bad news for him, but, much more importantly, it was very bad news for me. You see Mains has the contract to do all my combining this year. I could see that I would be carting him or his bicycle up and down the countryside, and doing all the road driving of his combine. I wasn't looking forward to that I can tell you.

But, Glory be! I'm in luck. Mains' blood sample showed what we had long suspected. Mains doesn't drink as much as it seems. He spills most of it.

Anyway, he got off.

24

Indulging my critical faculties

I PHONED Mossie on Friday. I just couldn't stand all this holidaying and not knowing how my harvest was ripening. Would he give me the excuse to hurry home early? "Oh dinna worry yersel. It has rained every day. Naething has done naething. Them wi thin croppies like yours are nae sae bad, but wi all the weet the disease is getting going in the rape, the barley's flat and the wheat is absolutely flat. The only crop that's kinda dry is the IACS and even there the forms are threatening to get wet."

I was phoning from what the Wasting Asset calls 'England's Green Unpleasant Land', to which the Breadwinner had dragged me to "get away from it all for a few days."

That's all very well for her that's a computerer and stares at a screen all day. But a farmer at the approach of harvest doesn't want away from the sight of his year's husbandry ripening towards the bank. Nor does he relish leaving his hill cows on the very week when, each year as sure as death, summer weed strikes any of them which is without a calf.

Still, when the Breadwinner says "jump", the Farmer who understands clearly his situation says: "How high, dear?"

Off we set. Nothing booked, we would just sweep south and look up a few old friends. That suited me fine because it gave me twelve hundred miles of farming, all the way to Stow-in-the-Wold and back.

I'd hate such journeys if I were a mere mortal. All he sees is another damned field and then another damned field.

But the farmer, the man of the soil, who is born of his father's acres and leaves them to his son, when *he* goes on a long overland journey, it is a fascinating viewing of other men's attempts at husbanding their heritage.

We saw how green Little Ardo was as we left her. A little too green. The fields should have been turning more towards harvest. And how yellow the spring rape. Surely it should

25

have been losing its petals by now.

The first signs of harvest were in Fife, but there was surprisingly little all down the west coast to Stow. There, there was some rape swathed and some barley cut, but they were just starting. To get harvest we had to cross to the east where Lincolnshire was disgorging another easy harvest from its great prairies.

In our six days away, for all Mossie's tales of rain, the harvest had moved north as far as Brechin - still a long way from Methlick.

And as England unfolded, I was able to amuse myself and indulge all the critical faculties honed on the plane stanes of Buchan. I was able to note that the thistle seemed to have been a major export for there were so many more south of the Border. And so many seem to be putting on their manure and their sprays with a shovel. They can grow wheat, but the striping in the barley spelt waste, environmental damage and rank bad farming all the way.

Yes, it did the heart good, and fairly made the journey shortsome.

I am reminded of the great James Low, who ran the work side of this farm for 44 years between the 1920s and the 1960s. We had got a new power-driven binder, a stunning innovation in its day. Now that would not have been dangerous had the binder not been on the tractor with the live drive.

What that meant was that, when you stopped because it had jammed again, you didn't only have to put the tractor out of gear. If you wanted to work safely, and if the tractorman wanted to take his foot off the clutch, you had to put the binder 'out of grip' as well.

To cut a long story short, the loon took his foot off the clutch when the grieve was unblocking. James had a suspected broken leg, and a great deal of pain when he was conscious. Luckily, that wasn't all the time, and he appeared to be more or less at rest when they put him into the ambulance and shut the door.

But no sooner had they done that, than a tremendous commotion of banging and shouting got up inside the ambulance. There was a rush to see what terrible thing had happened to the poor grieve next.

There he was, struggling to heave his torso up into a sitting position. "This is no use boys," he said "You'll need to sit me up so that I can see what my neighbours are daein a' the wey tae the hospital."

And finally a footnote on Mains, and the wonderful blood

26

sample that means he will be able to drive about the countryside in the next year, and that he can put the bicycle clips back in the press.

Well, the facts of the matter are that Mains' blood sample revealed that he had only fifty-four units of alcohol in his blood against a permitted maximum of eighty. Mains seemed very pleased about that, and so was I. It meant my combine would arrive this year without me having to go and drive it down.

Mains is a quiet lad and not by any means the most likely transgressor, so everyone else was pleased at his proven sobriety - except Gowkie. When he heard that Mains had been clear by such a wide margin he said, "What a pity. He could have had easy another nip, maybe twa."

Captain Ben - farming's local hero

BY FAR my most memorable sight of the week was of old Ben Coutts filling the ring with his presence at Banchory Show.

There is something heroic about Captain Coutts. He has for so long championed so much of what we love about our countryside. The wide open spaces, the farming of the hills and what was deemed to be good about life in the country before 'The Good Life'.

It has not been an easy row to hoe. Ben led the rearguard action of the native breeds against the invasion of foreign cattle in the seventies. As these proved their economic worth, coming top of test after test, Ben maintained that it was better to stick to the Aberdeen-Angus, the Galloways, the Shorthorns and the Highlanders. With the certainty that may have come from his upbringing in the manse, he was ideally placed to sponsor the view that black was white.

Ben was a councillor and a candidate for the Liberals before they became 'Democratic' and long before Christchurch. And throughout the long decline of the horse from the war onwards, he was there in every capacity, at so many shows, keeping the thing going.

Now, the Farmer could see Ben Coutts far enough for his part in the come-back of the horse as a pet. They dominate so many of the local shows that some of us who think the show should be about the business of farming, would like to see the horse put back in its place.

Nevertheless we had to admire Coutts at Banchory. There he was in the lashing rain, looking even more than his six foot three, now that he has lost weight. He was judging some high-stepping horses pulling manicured people in fancy carts. Despite his seventy-seven years he looked the last person to stop for a 'thunder-plump' as we used to call a cloud-burst.

To become a judge of horse these days you've first to act as an assistant on four occasions, and Ben had just such an apprentice with him. She was a very lucky lady, for Ben has judged every breed of cattle, dogs, pets, horse and crochetwork in his country life.

And he's a real judge. He shows who's boss.

At Banchory he pulled one youngster in first with a riding pony and would then put his assistant to ride it. The pony didn't fancy that, not realising how lucky he was to escape being ridden by the main judge, who would have been three stone heavier - and a whole world meaner.

"Riding pony's no damned use if it won't be ridden. Down to third place." The rider couldn't be blamed for sulking, but Captain Coutts wasn't for her showing it. "Any more of that and you're down to last." As there were twenty in the class there was no further bother.

And Coutts isn't afraid to take his own line. He added to his undying fame at the Royal Show in England when he judged the Burke Trophy for the best pair of beef animals. He could have chosen any of the three breeds, the societies for which he has run. He could have flattered his Royal audience by choosing the Queen Mother's Aberdeen-Angus, or he could have chosen, as most expected him to, between the new beef leaders, the Charolais and Simmental.

I don't know if the devil was prompting, but I'm sure there was a twinkle in his eye when he pulled the Old English Longhorn pair to be the beef champions for the year.

"They were the best pair. They were beautifully matched and none of the others could walk properly."

Maybe, but what about when he had to pick the overall supreme champion of the Orkney County Show? It would have taken a brave man to put anything other than the beef champion first in Orkney. Those who knew of his interest in horse might have thought Ben Coutts could go there for his champion. But he marched past all of those and the sheep, and the dairy cattle and the goats. After a careful inspection he chose the poultry champion - a rather splendid cockerel.

Would that there were more independent spirits like Ben. I was shocked by what I was told the other day by a very experienced show cattleman. He was blawing about his great year when he won just about everything there was to win on the north circuit. He had set himself to win nine of the biggest shows from Banchory to the Black Isle.

He saw one of the early shows as being critical to his success, "That would make three shows on the trot, and after that all the other judges would have to follow."

That really shook me.

Coutts wouldn't follow. Indeed I think the more shows a beast won, the more delight it would give him to put it down. And I wouldn't follow either, though in my case it wouldn't be cussedness but ignorance.

And so it was at Banchory on Saturday. I had the job of judging the Simmental Cattle.

It is a job which I enjoy and which I do not find in the least onerous. Some are surprised. "Isn't it a great responsibility?" Well, no. I am asked for my opinion and give it gladly. It is the person who asks me to be a judge who bears the burden of my perceived misjudgements. I'll soon line them up.

It is just as well that I take that attitude. I learned later that I had placed my champion above a bull that had been first at the Highland, and a cow which got a red ticket at Ingliston now has a nice blue one to go with it.

My champ was a calving heifer who was rising three years old and approaching a tonne. She didn't like me though. When I tried to handle her and check her udder she kicked me. "Aye, she kicked you last year at Keith an a'," said the cattleman, without remorse.

Old Coutts would have put her down to third for bad manners. But I needed a big champion to have a chance in the inter-breed, so up she went.

Strategy for sunshine was a complete failure

WE JUST may be in serious trouble. This forty days of rain after St. Swithin's is threatening us with the abyss once more. The last time we felt like this was in 1985 and '87. Then there were so many farms for sale in Buchan that that dreadful headline 'A County for Sale' was only a slight exaggeration. And, as I write, we are already eight days behind 1985. Far from lifting his rape, Mossie has had to stop ploughing his set-aside because the plough was sinking out of sight.

And I have nothing done, no barley cut, no rape swathed and no set-aside ploughed - on the 11th of August.

Much of the crop is still looking well from the road, but get in amongst it and see how every fungus known to man is on the march. The Red Rooster, president of the local branch of the 1000-acre club, was full of scorn this week. He had a visit from a green wellie man who looks after half a million acres in the South. His guest had complimented the Rooster on how clean his crops were looking.

"And ye ken we've got aathing in there except leprosy." Still, give the boys their due, they are hard to put down. The phone rang at lunchtime on Sunday. It was the Rooster himself. "T'hell wi this Charlie. If we canna mak money we can still mak merry. Four o'clock at the Salmon for sheetin clay doos and six o'clock barbecue. Wives and families invited."

It was a handsome offer, but who on earth throws a barbecue when the rain is sheeting off the byre roof and the drains are so full that the water is pouring down the close?

We decided to give the shooting a swerve, and arrived at six o'clock to find Mossie heaving the spare ribs onto the muckspreader he has converted to a mobile barbecue. The Breadwinner couldn't help hoping that he had washed the graip first. And there stood our

31

host, the shock of hair which is still mostly red despite the ravages of time, soaking with an emulsion of rain, pork fat and barbecue sauce.

With a wild look in his eye, and with some words the Breadwinner hadn't heard since she was at school, he told us about the injustice of it all. Ninety-nine times out of a hundred, if you arrange something in harvest time, the sun comes out and a strong breeze puts a rustle in the crop. You hate every wasted minute of the party. He had thought to tempt the Gods with a barbecue in the deluge, but it was a failure.

The rest of us were damned if we were to get wet, just to defy the fates. We left them to their barbecue and went to the bar to await the feast.

"Oh we of little faith."

It was rather touching though, looking out through the fog created by the rain cascading down on the red hot drum of the old rotaspreader. There were the two middle-aged men, with their middle-aged figures, in their Bermuda shorts and straw hats trying to convince a malign providence that a bit of sunshine would ruin their day.

It was a noble effort, and a great party for those of us who gave up immediately and stayed inside, but, as a strategy for sunshine, it was a total failure.

Of course it's not everyone who is down in the dumps just now. Big Hamish is on a high. He's just joined the 1000-acre club, and his success, if such it is, is partly due to the good St. Swithin himself.

The farm in question is called The Dunes and lies down to the North Sea on the east coast of Buchan. It is good snipe-shooting country and one year in five its heavy land can support a good crop of wheat. But with the hard times of the late eighties, and the water table as often above the ground as below, it had been sold to a developer who had visions of producing a new coastal village and making himself a fortune. For the last few years Big Hamish has had the eight hundred acres at a nominal rent.

And everything came right for the big man at once. The introduction of set-aside and acrcage payments meant that The Dunes, which had been abandoned to the wildlife, has now become attractive for growing aquatic crops like linseed, sunflowers, oil-seed rape and weeds. Then the developer gave up on the planning permission. And Hamish was able to buy on terms suitable to a sitting tenant.

Of course, there is the usual jealousy. Mossie's comment was withering. "Oh aye,

Hamish is in the 1000-acre club aaright - but only when the tide's oot."

Mossie was more at home at Turriff Show. We were there to present a long service medal to Bob Duncan who had been pigman at Moss-side for thirty-six years. I told Bob it seemed a hard way to earn a free entry into the agricultural shows. He agreed, but explained that he had been conned. He had signed up to work for the Auld Mossie, a very decent man, but then got caught when Mossie took over. By that time, his wife Harriet had invested too heavily in curtains and carpets, and a move was out of the question.

Anyway, it was a jolly occasion as we said a formal thanks to one of those who form the backbone of our industry. I stood my hand. Mossie stood his hand. And then, as was no more than our due, the president of the show took us into the committee rooms and stood both hands.

By this time Bob was in excellent fettle. "I'll need to stand my hand noo," he said. "I see the drink's ower there on the sideboard."

You don't work thirty-six years at Moss-side without learning a thing or two about economics.

August 23, 1993

Shooting from the combine

WE ARE just about through the curse of MacAskill. Saint MacAskill forecast, ad nauseam as though he were deliberately provoking the Gods, that, as it had rained on the 15th of July, there would be forty days of rain on the trot. Well, as I sit here, looking out at the sun driving the heavy dew off the backs of the cows, it looks as though we may at last get a day without rain. However the weather forecast is for showers in the afternoon. It is day thirty-five of the curse.

Though it has been a worrying time, I must confess myself a little disappointed that there are only five more days to go. There has been a refreshing black humour about, and something of the Dunkirk spirit has been in the air.

Mossie even gave up his day at the grice on the Inglorious Twelfth. Instead he decided to do his shooting from the combine. "Look at the money I'm savin, three thoosand pound for a start."

I can see you think you've spotted the snag in that: if it has been too wet for the grouse on the hills, what chance have they had at Moss-side? Well, you're right of course. But with the curse of MacAskill there is plenty of other shooting on what used to be the Mosses of Tarves and Gight. The snipe are back and you never saw duck that were fatter or more plentiful.

And there was even more saving. "I didna bother wi a professional loader, I jist took the wife. Aye, it could be tricky times ahead." In these days of political correctness there aren't many places left where you can "Jist tak the wife", even to save expense, but this neck of the woods is one of them.

Anyway, despite overnight rain yet again, we were able to start the combine on Sunday and I must say the whole business is a bit baffling. The grain is soft as porridge and yet two separate meters insist that it is below nineteen and fifteen percent moisture after thirty-two days of rain.

It is also baffling that the grain seems reasonably full. One of the gang has even got a sample of Manitou at a bushel weight of fifty-one pounds.

Now, Mossie has always said that winter barley doesn't need the sun and everyone else has always said that's just him trying to put folk off the scent. He does that you know, so you've got to watch him.

One year he had a bus load of crackshots up from the breadbasket of England, seeking the holy grail (Mossie's formula for the five tonne crop). He told them the secret was the timeous application of Straw-short as a pre-emergent spray. Unfortunately he forgot what he had told them. When they came back the next year and asked in puzzlement about the efficacy of Straw-short he told them, "Straw-short? A total waste of time."

It may be an accident, but it does seem possible that Mossie has been speaking the truth about winter barley not needing sunlight. His theory is that what it needs is just daylight and of course the further north you come the more of that you get in the summer time. Certainly there has been no sun to speak of this summer and yet there are indications that our barley may be reasonably heavy.

Ours is Pleasante and it varies between 61 and 63 point something. That is metric, so I don't really know what it is, except that it isn't very, very good, but neither is it bad like many expected it to be in so wet and sunless a year.

Certainly the old tractor seemed to think it was quite heavy. My first load came up the hill in first gear and the black reek billowing.

That could be because the old 590 really is going to die this time. On the other hand, it could be that the remains of the hand brake has jammed on again. And the fact that we have got a new bigger cart is bound to have something to do with it.

Nevertheless, the suspicion gradually snuck up that we may have a crop after all. I guess that we have nearly three tonnes and Mains, my neighbour and this year for the first time, contractor, says it will be, "gey near the three tonnes - maybe."

The field in which we had our winter barley always looks quite good from the road and yet it has always been disappointing at the mill, up till now. I bet Mossie he couldn't give me the advice that would give me a three-tonne crop off that field. He told me what to do. How much of what manure to put on, and when to strike with his secret brews.

All along it has looked as though he was winning his bet, but I knew of the ability of this field to flatter and to deceive. It has been nail-biting stuff. It's all away to the merchants now and, if I understand the tickets right, we have two tonnes eighteen.

Two tonnes fifteen is the worst we've had anywhere on the farm in recent years, but even so, two tonnes eighteen is good in such a year from such a field.

And it is a considerable consolation that my mysteriously poor field has beaten the great man. Not that you ever beat him. "Copper deficiency, that's the trouble. We'll sort it next year."

"And anyway, wi fifty-four pound o' subsidy and forty pound an acre for your strae you've as good as FOUR tonnes, never mind three."

I suppose I'll just have to pay up. After all, a gambling debt is a debt of honour.

That's him just been on the phone. "Go! GO! afore the rain comes on. Get that strae aff that park and get the ploo in. Have ye seen the price o' rape?"

There is no rest and I'm not even wicked.

Like the Sheik of Araby's palace

IT WAS a great relief on Friday, to find that the rape still had too high a moisture content to give me a reading. That meant that, with the winter barley away to the co-op for drying, and with the straw baled and barned, middle of harvest or not, The Farmer could go to the wedding.

I expected it to be the wedding of my year and I was not disappointed. Just for the record, the bride wore a gorgeous crinoline dress in which the family must have invested at least thirty fat lambs. (Being Perth Blackies their lambs are not that big.) The bridesmaids were in a fetching peach ensemble and the men and boys wore kilts.

But that is enough of that. There is always too much said and written about the young folk at weddings. The parents are what counts.

Indeed that fact is acknowledged in the way we refer to various weddings past. Thus when George Mackie married off the first of his three daughters to the strains of the Forfar brass band and the buzzing of a record number of champagne corks, that beautiful sunny day passed into legend. It is known to all who were there, and many more who can only wish, as 'George's wedding'. If you called it 'Diana Mackie's wedding', no one would know to what you referred. Similarly when I got the oldest Investment safely wed in among some moneyed lawyers, that came to be known as 'Charlie's wedding'. And quite right too.

On Saturday it was 'Bert's wedding'. He's a contractor from Angus, but you may well know him from his hobby of showing cattle all the way up to Smithfield. Bert Paton lives on his wife Patsy's family farm of the Spott at Glenprosen. Bert and Patsy have two and a half thousand acres of good hill, a thousand Blackface ewes and sixty Black cows.

The farm must be one of the most perfectly situated in Scotland. It sits at about a thousand feet up one of the prettiest glens in Angus on the flood plain of the Prosen, a

37

tributary of the Esk. Bert has put up a wonderful range of cattle courts, indoor buchts, shelters and barns. Spott is, as Mossie would put it if he were the owner, "a show".

And on Saturday, pride of place went to an enormous marquee, of the kind they have at Wimbledon and the Open golf tournament. It wasn't a proper canvas tent like we had for the Recovery Stock's wedding last year. It didn't even have four complete walls. One whole side was glass so that we could look out at the sun beating down on the Glen.

No. It was all flounces of muslim like one of the Sheik of Araby's desert palaces. Indeed had there been more bare bellies and fewer beer bellies you could have imagined you were indeed in the Orient.

Bert and I used to go the Highland Games together and toss the cabar, but now we don't have one good knee between us. So we spent a good deal of the time doing what men with bad knees can do at a dance: we chewed the fat.

When we were at that, Bert's son approached and bravely took up a seat beside the two old men. He told me that he was about to graduate, at which Bert snorted, "Hisna got a job."

Well I have nothing to tell anybody about getting on with sons, but it did seem to me that, on the day of his daughter's wedding, Bert could have shown a little more charm towards his son and currently front-runner for the rightly sought-after position of his heir.

I took the lad's side. "Well done Archie. I wish I had a son a graduate." If Bert was impressed he was damned if he was going to show it.

I shouldn't have said it to such a distinguished graduate of the school of life, but I had taken the boy's part now. "Well he's got a degree Bert. That's mair than you've got."

He's a big man, and has the sort of presence that only people who have done it themselves have. I started to feel smaller even before he spoke. He looked up at the glittering chandeliers, and round his desert palace at the well-heeled, fed and watered guests who were still trying to find immortality in the Champagne he had imported specially for the occasion.

Holding his great arms wide to embrace it all, and with conviction and scorn for lesser qualifications, he said, "That is my degree."

Young lads are hard to impress these days, but young Archie disappeared and a few minutes later, the Spott tups which are being prepared for the top ring at Perth in the back-end, came trotting past the window. I don't know whether it was a marketing exercise, or whether they were just rubbing it in to the other side, who would likely shop at Castle Douglas for their tups.

I think I could have persuaded Bert at that moment that, while a degree is an undoubted handicap, it doesn't mean you canna do anything.

It was the second time Bert had put me in my place like that. He had been visiting me twenty years ago and I took him to see Gight Castle. Then we both had Simmental cattle and a neighbour had some in the castle park. It was a fine day, and it's a very bonny spot, so off we went. I remarked casually and quite correctly that Lord Byron's mother had been a daughter of the laird of Gight castle.

"Oh aye," said Bert, "and wha's he?"

39

Like a good intellectual snob I was shocked. Imagine not knowing who Lord Byron was. But like a bad intellectual snob I let my horror at Bert's ignorance show.

"Oh come on, Bert. You must know Lord Byron - the poet?"

"No. What did he write, like?"

And you know, I couldn't name one damned poem.

Laugh is on green welly brigade

I'M AFRAID there's no holding Mossie any longer. But before I tell you all about his wonderful crop of sunflowers, I'd better get you up to date with how things are going, here on the little hill that looks down on the Vale of Ythan.

We've got our two tonnes eighteen of Pleasante winter barley safely away to the co-op at little over seventeen percent moisture. Another year of low drying charges seems imminent. The rape, having lain for seventeen days, has come in in the best of order, but we don't yet know the moisture or the quantity. It looks good though and anything less than a tonne and a half will be regarded as a disaster.

We're two to three weeks behind normal but, thanks to modern techniques of harvesting, there is no harm done yet. Everything is standing and weeds are few, so the delay isn't too worrying. Some of my neighbours who specialise in crops with foot diseases, or who put on too much nitrogen and so grow horizontal crops, are suffering heavy losses. But those who grow the vertical kind are alright, thus far.

And it's thanks to the modern machinery that we have not yet fallen behind with the sowing. The winter rape went in in pouring rain after the curse of MacAskill had run its forty days but it was still raining. The secret is to plough and sow at the same time. Even apparently sodden ground is reasonably workable underneath, so you send a six furrow plough down the field with a drill machine scurrying after it with the seeds.

There has been the odd disaster, of course. On Sunday morning there was a phone call when all decent people (and certainly all those with hangovers) were still in bed. "Cows on the road."

"Well," I thought, "I'd better go and help whoever it was to get his cows back to safety. After all, you never know when it might be your own."

True, true. And as you may have guessed, they were indeed mine. Some cows, who were old enough to know better, but not

41

old enough to remember when it was last used as a gate, had forced open an old gate in the Howe park and were onto the free range system.

I got them home with the help of some neighbours who could see that it might be their turn next.

But the star turn this week has been Mossie and his crop of sunflowers. There is a big EC subsidy to grow these, and despite the fact that he was told period, all are now in bloom, and, if you believe Mossie, they are producing their own sunshine and encouraging the growth in the other aquatic plants, like linseed, he has sown in the moss.

What really made him do this crazy thing was a bus load of green welly men who laughed at him when they were touring and came to Moss-side. They said it couldn't be done. But they said Beethoven was mad,

it was impossible to grow them in North Britain, he took on the job in the wettest bit of the moss he could find.

And grow?

They are a show!

Despite seeing the sun for only four days in their growing they said van Gogh was mad and they said Hitler was mad. The difference with Mossie is that he is mad.

And he fairly can grow sunflowers. He sowed fifteen plants to the square metre and there are eleven flowering now

He's even gone on the tele to confuse everyone with the explanation of how to do it.

Now, I'll bet you think you've seen the snag. How is he going to get the seeds to ripen and the stems to dry, so that he can get the combine in and harvest the seeds for their sunflower oil?

Not a problem. It says you are supposed to make a reasonable attempt to harvest them but it doesn't say they have to be ripe. He is harvesting them in flower and selling them to the shops at a pound a bloom. Mrs Moss, dear sweet creature that she is, sat up in bed one night when the Happy Faces were just coming out, and said: "You know what you should do? You should put a box beside the field and have Pick-Your-Own, and give the money to charity".

"T'hell wi charity," says Mossie. "I'm takin this to the Salmon Inn to treat the boys."

That was indeed a noble sentiment (on Mossie's part), but yet again there was a snag. Many as are the friends of Mossie, and much as that band increased when it was learned that he was buying, there was no way he could spend it all at the Salmon.

While, at the Salmon, we're queueing up to spend it, back at the Moss a constant procession of florists' vans is loading up. There are loads for Aberdeen and for Inverness. At first it was just a few hand-picked, but after his tele appearance he decided to mechanise. He yoked the swather and now offers delivery from a bulker. It will blow the blooms into your warehouse. An artic left last night for Birmingham and Mossie is hoping that some of the green-welly men who said it couldn't be done will see them.

And what is the secret of growing sunflowers in these northern climes in a sunless summer? Well, I do happen to know, but there is no use telling you. The fact is, Mossie doesn't know either. You see, what he did was, every time he sprayed any of his thousand acres with anything, he swilled the tank out and sprayed it on the sunflowers. You need a place to do that to prevent the washings going down the drains and causing pollution, so Mossie put the swillings on the sunflowers. He must have got the dosages exactly right but I don't see how he can repeat it. He'll never get a coincidence like that again.

Cruellest cut of all at hairst

THE FARMER is feeling a bit small. I am laird of all I survey - as long as I don't look very far. And that's just the snag.

My father sat here and dominated the village. He was a big farmer with six men to see that he didn't have to do a hand's turn. Although I have twenty more acres, I cannot afford even one man. I am a crofter or a sma' hudder at best.

This was brought home cruelly to me this week, and in several ways.

First, it was the story about my cousin Maitland Mackie who, as well as a hundred and fifty other things, is the Vice President of the Scottish National Farmer's Union. He had decided to keep one of the combines going over lunchtime. In the neighbouring parish of Tarves, he had three working on a six hundred acre spread that had been recently added to the empire.

When he arrived in the field it was already dinner time and the men had gone home. They had finished the field they were in, so Maitland opened the gate, jumped aboard the shiniest-looking combine and started filling the tank.

Things were going well. The sun was shining and the corn was rustling as the reels swept it into the great mobile thrashing machine. In a very little time Jack Sleigh, the former President of the Royal Highland and Agricultural Society, appeared in the field. Maitland knew that Jack was one of his new neighbours and was pleased that he had stopped for a chat.

Soon he was up in the cab of the combine and exchanging the usual pleasantries. Then it was "What like a run are you getting?"

"Oh grand. Look for yourself. Its fine and dry, and a good bold sample."

"That's good," said Jack, "for this is my field."

So you see, with cousins like that, it is no wonder I am feeling like a crofter today. That's big. Imagine being so big you could even not know which were your own fields.

And my pals among the

grain barons have been making me feel a bit out of it too.

You see, harvest is the climax of the year. It is when those who have done well for a year reap the rewards and those who have done badly have to tell lies. It is the time for blawing about your successes and pouring doubt on the successes of others. It is the time to shake your head at the prospects for survival of those who have got it wrong. It is a time of living at high tension.

And for the big boys, that tension goes on and on. From the winter barley to the spring rape the harvest could easily last from late July to early October. But with my hundred and fifty acres of combinable crops, I have only a series of short bursts. One day cut the winter barley. One day cut the winter rape. It could take two days for the wheat, and another two days for the spring rape.

So there are six days when I can go down to the Salmon Inn and join in the action replays. But for the res' of the time I am put in my place. I can either listen to the rest blawing, or sit in the corner with my half pint. My twenty-seven acres of winter rape gave me a record for the farm of thirty-three cwts at twelve percent moisture. That did make them sit up for one day, but it was soon forgotten as, day after day, Mossie would blaw about the hundred acres he'd cut, and the Red Rooster would speculate on how much water he'd need to add to his hundred and fifty tonnes of barley to get it up to fifteen percent.

You see, if you want to be one of the top boys, you have to have your own combine. And it is no use having a third-hand banger costing ten thousand. If you are big enough, your harvest goes on and on. Mossie cut a hundred and twenty acres of barley one day and then he and Crookie and the Rooster nearly ran me off the road, as they sped along on their combines to the next venue. Next day they were back in the pub having cut seventy acres for the Rooster.

It is a very hard club to get into. Just how hard was brought home to me last week when Mossie broke the main drive shaft of his combine. Everyone was, of course, highly delighted, though they pretended to be most sympathetic. But our man is hard to beat. That same day he was back in action with the biggest newest dearest combine on loan from the sellers "for a demonstration".

It was a wonderful machine. The only complaint Mossie could make at it, was that the computer was slow to

work out the arbitrage rates between the Chicago and London grain futures markets. After a day of driving this thing he was all ready to buy. The tactic of giving him a demonstration had worked.

"How much to change?"

"Taking into account your old one being two years old - £75,000," said the salesman.

That made even Mossie gasp. He decided just to have it a bit longer on trial.

So you see why the Farmer feels a bit small.

And worse than that, rumour has it that Crookie is going to buy one of these new monsters for "a negotiable six figure sum". Mind you, that was before Mhairi was born. Imagine having to start saving for a wedding at forty, and Mhairi is only the start. Still you can't help envying him. He is so taken up with his issue that he hasn't been down to see the boys since she was born.

Cows far from happy with what was left

NOT HAVING eaten much of it in my time, I'm a bit out of my depth when it comes to the eating qualities of grass, and yet I can tell you that our grass at the moment is below average.

I have roughly a hundred cows and calves running on what we call the Braes - and they are displeased. In fact it is worse than that. They are parading the fence and roaring their heads off. And yet there is far more of the green stuff among their feet than there was on the spring day. Then they were so glad to be out filling themselves with the sweet green leaves.

The lack of sunshine, combined with years of nitrogen rather than grazing compounds, does finally appear to be taking its toll.

I had been intending to make a second cut of silage but, as the rain came sheeting down, I could see that there would be few bales, and that the chances of getting anything as dry as silage broth were slim. Anything we were to conserve would be consomme.

So we let the old dears and their calves in amongst it. That fairly proved the point. The stuff was so wet and fusionless, that they were soon scouring over their necks. Within a few days most of the proposed winter keep was gone, and they were roaring their dissatisfaction with what was left.

I have started feeding them a bit of straw, but that is to be the mainstay of their diet from now 'til April, and they can have too long of that. It is not the low cost system we are aiming for, but I must start feeding them a couple of pounds of cobs on the grass.

And how am I going to replace the second cut silage?

The clever thing is probably to sell the young stock at the last of the calf sales. That's certainly what Mossie thinks I should do. "Dinna be a workin feel. Give yoursel an easy life." But I have to keep my bull

calves till the New Year to collect Mr MacSharry's gold, and by that time it will look tempting to keep them for the spring madness that comes with the first show of green in the fields.

No, the problem of the missing silage is easily solved and, surprisingly, economically too. I will buy in a couple of hundred bales. We have neighbours, much better farmers than me, who have grown mountains of silage and good stuff can be had for about seven pounds a bale.

Now, that cannot be dear. It costs getting on for a fiver to make the stuff. But what really makes buying "on" is the price of straw. It is making a great trade and like to get better if this weather continues.

Mossie sold a hundred acres of winter barley straw a few weeks back and averaged six pounds and seventy pence a bale for it. Of course I know I'll not get as much as him, for it is not my shoulder upon which the devil perches, but even at a fiver it is surely worth paying two pounds to turn straw into good silage.

Indeed I think I'll stop making silage and buy it in every year. The net effect of the EC reforms is that cereals are so profitable that we will grow more, not less.

But what about set-aside? Surely that is reducing the amount that is grown. Well yes, but not much. Set-aside is replacing spring rape in our rotation. That means from April to September the set-aside ground lies fallow but the rest of the farm is fully cropped with winter barley and winter wheat, both eleven month crops, and winter rape which this year has had twelve months in the ground. And we're bringing twenty-five extra acres, just about fifteen percent of our cropping area, under the plough.

Better than that, if I want to be the 'workin feel' I am tempted to grow non-food crops on the set-aside. Certainly, Mossie is away with his shopping sunflowers. If he sells them for sunflower oil he has to count that in his cereal acres, but if sales to the shops hold up there'll be none left for the crushers.

And it's better than that. He grew the sunflowers in a bit of the moss that was too wet for the linseed. And that has given an unexpected bonus. On one of the few sunny days when they were busy with the PYO sunflowers, one customer asked if the beautiful blue flowers were for sale also. The blue of the linseed and the yellow of the happy faces made a picture as Mossie wrestled unsuccess-fully with his conscience over how much to charge.

So there's another crop as an alternative to set-aside.

Mind you, Mossie will need all the income he can get. He has a sixteen year old boy who is turning out to be something of a crackshot at the clay doo shooting. And Mossie has just figured out why his son is always anxious to go to the outfarm in the next parish to do odd jobs. At first he assumed it was just that the provisional licence meant he could now drive on the roads, and of course, with a tractor you don't need an experienced passenger.

But that wasn't it at all. When Mossie went down to the shooting lodge for a pint at lunchtime on Thursday, he was astonished to find that he could hardly get into the car park for his enormous Ford tractor. Russell was down for a shot with his fifty thousand pound runaround.

You might have thought Mossie would be angry, but those of us who know him could see that there was just a hint of the "That's my boy," about it. "I ken exactly what the little *****'s up to. I used to dae the same masel."

Things get trickier all of the time

WHEN MY father and mother went off to fight the Huns they left me me alone but with a philosophy. You see, both my parents were socialists. Yes they were. I know it seems odd that they were and that a farmer like me should admit it freely in these days of collapsed communism and unrestrained capitalism. But it is true.

Almost my first words were, "Workers of the world unite. You've nothing to lose but your chains." It is true that I thought that slogan was something to do with the bicycle. When I got a tricycle with pedals, I could see the importance of a chain and was puzzled as to what good it would do the workers to lose theirs. Anyway, cycling was clearly going to be tricky under socialism, but I supposed there would be other consolations.

Perhaps it was their failure to explain socialism clearly enough, but when I went to stay with my Tory grandparents in 1942, I was ripe for conversion. In no time I was thoroughly schooled in the dogmata of capitalism.

Whenever my grandparents would have guests, which was every morning coffee time and every afternoon tea time, I would wait for a lull in the conversation. In the drawing room of Mary and Maitland Mackie that might be quite a long time, but I was patient. Then when space allowed, a little voice would pipe up, "I believe in private enterprise," and a determined little fist would beat on the arm of the great settee.

That earned me hoots of happy laughter every time, and as much as a shilling from my friends among the capitalists. Socialism faced an uphill struggle.

I was reminded of the early attempts to indoctrinate me by Mossie's coaching of his daughter Jill, who is now two years old and still forty years younger than the grain Baron.

At first it was pure commercialism. At the height of his attempts to corner the market for sunflower blooms, Mossie would say: "And how's

Daddy going to make his fortune?" and if she felt like it Jill would reply: "Out of Happy Faces."

That helped to sell the blooms at a pound a piece - and helped to rub in the message to all those who said he couldn't grow sunflowers in Aberdeenshire.

But now Jill has been moved on to where my parents started me fifty years ago. She is into the propaganda of agri-politics.

"What do the farmers say?" asks the father.

"Tricky times ahead," pipes up the two year old.

It's a good laugh and all very sweet the first couple of dozen times, but it does get tiring, especially as it is so true.

It was bad enough trying to work out exactly how much of the farm not to plough up in order to get your AICS form right, but the thing is getting trickier, all the time.

Gone are the days when you could just grow as much of what you thought would pay, for as little as possible, and sleep easy in your bed. Now we have a planning nightmare to negotiate. Which crops should be missed out of the rotation for set-aside? Should we set our worst fields aside as the system is bound to break down before we get to the good ones?

Which of the bewildering array of non-food crops should we grow on the set-aside? Can Mossie grow his sunflowers on set-aside next year? Surely he can as long as he sells them at the flowering stage. And should we all be putting all our set-aside into sunflowers or might that flood the market? Should we sell the cow quota and put the money against an old age that is fast approaching?

So it is tricky times ahead.

I had them this week. We managed to get all the muck out for the first time for many years. I got Davie the contractor to come with two mucking carts - and Potions, who used our one.

Now, you will recall the scorn that the Wasting Asset poured on my head for letting silage wrap and baler twine get in amongst the muck. I told him then that I was too old to change, and that if the odd bit of bale net did get in amongst the muck, and if it did mean we had to get into the carts to free the hammers that throw the muck out over the fields occasionally, so be it.

As a father, it fills me with pride to be able to say that my son was, for once, quite right. As long as I live I will never let another foreign body in amongst the straw in the cattle courts.

My mind was quickly made up early, when all three carts were choked. The prospect of idle carts and men contracted by the hour is too much. They scratched their heads. They wondered if they should go home for the gas burner, and they wouldn't touch the carts till they had been power hosed clean.

It was 'tricky times ahead' all right. These modern young men were obviously feared at muck. There was nothing else for it. I put one on the digger and I spent the rest of the two days inside one cart after another, cutting string and tearing at net with my bare hands, while the other two lads kept any carts that were clear, going.

The worst of it was that Mossie saw my humiliation. As usual when all is not well, he happened past. "Tricky times ahead," he said delightedly when he saw my head sticking out of the cart. "You're going through a bad patch."

He disappeared to see what he could find to criticise among my crops. He was back in minutes. "Tricky times are here! The slugs have demolished your rape. You'll hae to reseed it."

He was right, of course, and that was just what I did next.

Great ice cream bash had aplomb

THERE IS no doubt what was the big event this week. It was the opening of Mackie's new Ice Cream Dairy - "and don't you dare call it a factory". When, in an industry in which what used to be a big farm can be run single-handed, you come upon a farmer employing 285, you have to take notice.

Anyway, the boys have been getting excited for weeks. "Half a million pounds for a shed? Good god, they could have got another three hundred acres for that." "Or four new combines," sang the scandalised Grain Barons.

Not even the fact that the wheat had finally got below thirty percent moisture on the last day of September, could divert us from the prospect of the great bash planned by Maitland Mackie.

There were to be two hundred sat down to lunch for a start. "Aye," said Mossie, "and it's jist the top boys that are to be there. I suppose the invitations'll be oot afore lang." I was sympathetic, of course, but I had to point out that the invitations were out already. And the Red Rooster wasn't there either and neither was Crookie.

When that was realised, the criticisms became freer. We would calculate the cost of the do. With the meal being produced by Marilyn Rattray, the finest restauranteuse and food technologist in the North-east, that would be bound to cost £25 a head we agreed. But Mossie wasn't going to be impressed now. He quickly worked out the price of beef, the price of soup and a bit fancy Pavlova, cheese and coffee. "That's naething. Jist a margin over feed of £20. That's what we get but we havna jist 200 visitors. We get that margin on 4,000 pigs."

There is no doubt that the boys not being there would keep the cost in champagne down, but we still couldn't see how the job could be done for less than the proverbial "undisclosed five figure sum".

So, after being put down for weeks as a mere 'sma' hudder' by the Grain Barons, I was very glad that Maitland wanted members of his family to carve for his guests and, having so many guests, had to invite even from among the clan's crofters.

We were determined to put on a show. I washed and even polished the Jaggy, emptied the feed bags out of her and vacuumed her lovingly. Potions would act as chauffeur. He would put on the Merchant Navy officer's hat which he hadn't needed since he was commissioned and became unemployably expensive.

The Breadwinner and the Farmer arrived in style. Maybe with my carving knife sticking out of my top pocket I should have made for the tradesmen's entrance, but it was grand to swish past the car park and right up to the door. And, of course, with a chauffeur one has a certain other freedom.

I was delighted to see that the sheik's palace had been removed from Bert's wedding and erected on the lawn. Our comforts were clearly to be taken care of in style.

We started with coffee and a welcome from old Sir Maitland who, with his father, had started the business in the 1930s. He told us that he had nearly gone into ice cream in 1946, and indeed, had bought some machinery for the job from an Italian. The sums

looked good, but in those days of rationing he could only get half a ton of sugar a year so he had to give up. Certainly the current Maitland is luckier, and that's a good thing as he'll need a good deal more than half a tonne to make the six million litres of ice cream he'll be producing if his new factory ever works flat out.

Mind you, there are worse things for an ambitious farmer than a lack of sugar. Old Sir Maitland was able to sell his ice cream-making machinery at a handsome profit.

Then it was off to see some of the twenty-five hundred acres and very polished acres they were. It isn't like a farm at all; no smell, no strang, and hardly even any dust or dubs. They've deep-pointed the few bits of stonework which are all that remain of the old steading, planted trees and flowers everywhere, and the piece de resistance is the old waterwheel that once ground the oats for men and horses. It has been restored for the price of a new car, and you may be sure that it was a fairly up-market car.

Sir Alistair Grant has done well for himself in the 36 years since he was milking cows in Lincolnshire. As boss of the Argyll and Safeways supermarket businesses, he was guest of honour. I bet he could see no resemblance to his days on the land in the new ice cream dairy he opened. There is nothing but gleaming chrome pipes and a few people with plastic space suits wandering about.

And the tour ended on carts to which we mounted by specially constructed stairs. We sat on rugs on bales of straw and viewed this extraordinary outfit. Most of the firm's 1000 cows seemed to be there carpeting the howe in black and white as we made our way up through the 100 acres which Mackie can afford to put into nurseries and trees. We stopped at the top of the hill beside the lagoon into which 30 million gallons of slurry and 38 million gallons of dirty washing water are pumped every year.

As the autumn breezes brought a hint of winter down from the Grampians, our guide commended the 360 degree view to us. "Away up there to the north you can see the Moray Firth, over to the east you can see the North Sea and to the south that's Bennachie. And, on a really clear day, it is even possible to see the tip of Mr Mackie's overdraft."

Tricky times ahead but all is not gloom

MOSSIE IS right as usual. With October wearing on there is hardly a blade of wheat cut in Aberdeenshire, and though most of the rape is swathed, it is as green as the newly breered winter barley. It really is 'tricky times ahead'. Every day, at least twenty times, he asks Jill, his two year old late baby, "What does the farmer say?" And, maybe eighteen times a day she obliges with, "Tricky times ahead."

But all is not gloom. Not by any means. The old-fashioned harvest, the harvest of combines, tractors and bad language, may be headed for disaster, but there is the new harvest to consider. The twice-yearly harvest from Brussels is quite independent of the weather, and it is going splendidly.

The rape cheques are in, and they have spread a great deal of happiness over this sodden land.

Young Ochyoch, who two to three years ago gave up his steady job for three hundred bare acres in a peaty part of Aberdeenshire called 'the New Pitsligo Triangle', was particularly happy about the Brussels harvest. In fact his wife phoned up Big Hamish's Mrs and crowed: "The rape cheques are in. I'll race you to the bank."

She did too, and then the two happy wives got a start to spend it. They celebrated with a poke of chips each from the 'Crispy Fryer'.

The Farmer was pleased with his cheque too. He showed it to the Breadwinner, who has always been a bit unkind about the ability of the old-fashioned harvest to produce income. And even she was impressed with the Brussels harvest. Then I phoned the banker.

"This is MR Allan here. Brace yoursel. I'm comin doon wi the rape cheque."

Never have so many useless crops done so much good to so many balance sheets.

Not everybody got a cheque mind. Mossie didn't, and he was not pleased.

Normally, the manure would have hit the fan. Anyone who had got between Mossie

and what he thought he was due, would have been in dead trouble. But the lad was genuinely worried. After all, he remembered what happened to me last year, when I had made that silly clerical error which would have awarded me an extra five hundred pounds.

Like me he wouldn't have done it deliberately, but suppose he had made a mistake and they had found him out? Would they be going to fine him twice the error as they are quite entitled to do?

He decided on the coward's way out and went down to the Salmon for a pint. He had been sipping pensively for a few minutes when the barmaid said, casual like, "By the by, Mossie, there's a letter for you." It was the rape cheque for four hundred acres.

Mossie had been assing about when he had filled up the form and, where it asked where he wanted them to send the cheque had snorted, "Whar dae they think, for god's sake? They may as well pit it straight doon tae the pub. Maist o' it's gaun there onyway." His secretary, good obedient girl that she is, had filled in the form accordingly, and he had signed it.

Yes the Brussels harvest has been a joy. And we need all the joy we can get, for the old-fashioned harvest is no more than a distant prospect.

I took a sample in the last week of September, when I would expect to be taking my first wheat cheque to soothe the banker. I knew it wasn't ready, but I wanted a figure to start with. Then each time I would have a lower figure; it would give me something to blow about and it would be encouraging.

It was not encouraging. Instead of that hard crackling sound grain makes in the grinder when it is ready, this stuff made not a sound. I had to scrape it out with my finger in the manner of one getting a tasty lick from the top of an old-fashioned milk can. (Oops. Shouldn't have admitted to knowing what that was like - but wasn't it good?)

Of course I got no reading at all. It is the only time I have seen juice running out of a moisture metre.

Mossie has cut some wheat "just to give the drier something to dae". But he has to fill it twice for each batch, or even three times. He fills her up and within minutes the close is filled with dense steam. After a couple of hours it has shrunk and is only half full and he has to fill her up with some more porridge. He was moaning into his pint on Saturday afternoon when he announced gloomily, "I suppose I'd better gang away hame and check the steamer."

One good thing about this incredible weather, is that it has put paid to the nonsense about Mossie's sunflowers. Fair enough, he grew them and confounded the experts, but it has been a bit tiring for the rest of us.

He really sees himself as an artist. He's even got little Jill answering the phone with, "Van Gogh here."

We have all done our best to be pleased for him that, in the wettest year the North-east has ever seen, he was able to make a wee fortune out of shopping sunflowers. But show me the farmer in Aberdeenshire who says he is not taking comfort from the fact that the Monsoon has put paid to any grand notions that sunflowers might count as a combinable crop this year, and I'll show you a liar.

Of course he'll try to get away with it, subsidy and all, by claiming that he has already harvested the field as flowers. But the few honest men in Aberdeenshire admit that on this issue, they are on the side of the taxpayers. The subsidy is for growing sunflower oil not 'Happy Faces'.

October 18, 1993

A last pint at the Salmon Inn

IT'S TRICKY times ahead alright. There is no wheat and no spring rape harvested in Aberdeenshire. Almost all the potatoes are still in the ground and we're into the third week in October.

It's times like this I'm glad my first ancestor here built his house upon the hill. My grandfather used to say of Little Ardo, "It's a place that'll neither drought nor droon." Fair enough, but as I look down on the river Ythan, swollen in spate, and see the rain sheeting down off the porch roof, I do wonder how much more rain it would take to reach the front door. Really I shouldn't worry. My margin for error is only down from 130 feet to 123.

I had a phone call from Crookie on Monday. He and Mossie were going down to the Salmon "for a last pint. It's aboot all we can dae".

Not true. Of course there's something we can do: we can complain about it.

Mossie says this is already worse than 1985. "It dried up in October and we got it all tidied up," he says. But at least Mossie hasn't got any potatoes. Poor Crookie has seventy acres which cost £1200 an acre to grow and they're saturating along with the rape and the wheat. Who will put shoes on little Mhairi's feet?

And for once I beat Mossie. While he is glad he has no tatties to lift, I am gladder that I have none either. The Red Rooster paid a king's ransom for my quota so he has to lift my sixteen acres while I can go down to the bank and look at his money.

Yes, that may be the future for farming. For the EC wizards have just awarded me another magic asset. I have been informed this week that I am the proud owner of the right to subsidies on 39.6 cattle.

That's an interesting number don't you think? I'm told I'll be able to sell my quota and that looks like the best bet if the potato quota is anything to go by. The value is only there in so far as the crazy regime under which we operate is still in place. But surely that cannot last. I wish I had a milk quota to sell.

As we sipped our third 'last pint' Mossie started to look on the bright side. We'd just heard that there is a danger that set-aside may be doubled. Next year we may have to grow weeds on 30 percent of our proposed cereal acreages. "It's tricky times ahead, but this extra set-aside will help. Nae problem though it rains all year wi' set-aside."

And I'm beginning to see his point. One of the troubles with the flood is we can't get on with sowing next year's crop. And yet, as I look out of my study, I can see a very strong crop of winter barley struggling above the waves on what was last year's set-aside. If I'd had another twenty acres of set-aside I'd have had a small but guaranteed income off it and I'd have had an extra twenty acres of healthy winter barley promising a bounteous harvest next year.

He'll never do it, of course, but Mossie even allowed himself the thought that Aberdeen-shire would have to give up cereals and swing back to cattle and sheep.

He'd give it no more thought if he'd had a week like I've had. You see, this week we weaned forty-three calves. (Or is it the forty-three cows you wean?)

Anyway the havoc that forty-three calves can wreak trying to get to forty-three udders is prodigious. And, knowing that, I determined to imprison the calves in our securest sheds, and put as many fences as possible between the cows and the steading. I knew that our fences were not the best.

That carefully worked out strategy was quite inadequate to the job in hand.

The cows knew exactly where their little treasures were, and lined up along the fence in the field below the one in front of the house. The calves were in sheds at the back of the house so, from where the cows were standing, the calves might have been in the house and there was no doubt that the straightest line to their calves was through the Breadwinner's beloved garden.

Tricky times were clearly ahead.

I don't know if the best fence in the world would have held the fond forty-three but my ancient stragglers had no chance. They lined up and roared and pushed and roared and pushed until the fence collapsed.

They careered over the field

60

towards the steading and their calves. A couple of circuits of the field and a few picks at the grass in the fresh field and they were all lined up at the Breadwinner's garden fence, roaring, leaning and pushing. After a whole summer without footholes in the lawn my life was once again set to become a misery.

Then I was given one of those flashes of genius which crises can provoke. I grabbed a bag which had, until that morning, contained North Eastern Farmers' cattle feeding cobs. I ran down to the field, opened the gate at the corner and called to them that it was feed time.

They may have thought I had relented and was taking them back to their calves, or they may have thought they were to be fed, but the forty-three of them ran after me, through the close and into the piggery. Luckily it was empty and I was able to imprison them there. It took four days of bawling before they remembered how nice it is not to have progeny around.

If I sound a little weary today, it's not just the weather. There's the lack of sleep as well.

As we had our fourth 'last pint' Mossie cheered us all up. "Well boys there is this. Look at the tax we'll save." Then, looking at Crookie, "We're right lucky we pay forty per cent tax. Poor auld Charlie, he's only saving 25 per cent."

It's tricky times indeed when you have to take consolations like that.

Staggering cow would not die

I KNOW fine that you don't want me to tell you all my troubles, but it is difficult to avoid it, with November looming and the wheat and spring rape still in the fields. I am two-thirds the way through the harvest, and have not turned a wheel for six weeks.

Anyway, here is the good news.

The cow that I saw going down with staggers this week, didn't die. I was off into town when I saw this old Blue Grey going down, in full view of the main road.

I am not often lucky with staggering cows and might have been tempted to look away, but that wasn't possible in full view of the road. I really must get a car phone, for it would have saved me going into the house to call the vet before grabbing my bottle of magnesium and my trusty needle, and hurrying back to my cow.

She was the usual spasmodic wreck, but not dead like the one we had this time last year.

The vet who looked after us when I started to farm twenty years ago, told me that the best way was to inject your litre of magnesium in as many sites as possible all over the beast's body. That I did, rather than using the more conventional flutter-valve to put the whole lot under the skin.

That done, I proceeded to to haul the old dear round as she was on a steep slope and had landed head downhill. To my amazement, as soon as she was level, she scrambled to her feet and stood there shivering. By night she was walking about only a little stiffly, and by morning she was quite recovered. And the vet hasn't touched her.

Mind you, the outlook isn't very good. She has a choice of ad lib minerals, a new fangled magnesium lick and magnesium syrup. Yet she still went down with magnesium deficiency. So how long till she goes down again? Next time I may not be on my way to Aberdeen and she certainly won't still be in a field next to the road.

The next good news I have for you is that I don't have any pigs. My piggery has a capacity of four hundred or so and it is quite empty.

What a relief! Pigs are losing about fifteen pounds a piece at the moment. I have a neighbour who produces over a quarter of a million of them a year, so he's suffering.

Then again, I don't have any potatoes. That is another joy, for the rain has washed the topsoil off, exposing them to frosts which have already reached five degrees.

Apart from that, all I can say on the positive side is that the Wasting Asset gets his licence back at the end of the month. There is no chance that he will have learned his lesson, but at least he'll be available for a while as a go-for.

Of course Mossie is making a much better job than me of looking on the bright side. We're getting fed up of his warnings of "Tricky times ahead," when the tricky times are so obviously here. For a start, Little Ardo has only one bale of straw per head to see the cattle through the winter. And it seems impossible that we'll get the wheat until November.

Anyway, his latest is to lick the cigar to the other side of his mouth and say gravely, "It's times of opportunity. When aabody else is in trouble that's when you can get a bargain. And there's going to be bargains galore in Aberdeenshire. It's 'A County for Sale' aa ower

AH'LL BOOK IN FOR TWA JUMPS ... IN CASE THE FIRST EEN DISNA WORK!

MOSSIE'S BUNGIE JUMPING

SPECIAL RATES FOR FARMERS

again."

Certainly the gallows humour is back. Mossie's first bargain is a 100 foot crane, off which he is offering Bungie jumping with special rates for farmers. For very little extra he won't tie the ropes too tight and Crookie has booked two jumps, "In case the first een disna work."

But the one I feel most for is young Ochyoch. This is only his third harvest and it is not a pretty sight. He was farms manager on a big estate and bravely took on fully three hundred acres when the laird decided to stick to being a landowner (for which he was bred), rather than a farmer (for which he was not).

Ochyoch is just the sort of lad our industry needs. He's got a sense of humour, he's not frightened to take a risk, and he's not afraid of hard work either. As well as doing all his work himself, he's been working 'full time' milking cows for a neighbour.

And he's not short of heirs to carry on after him. There are three little Ochyochs who are just about at the stage when they'll start to be more of a help than a hindrance about the farm. In a few years they'll be ready for the next 'Time of Opportunity.'

But with the rape, the wheat, and the spring barley all caught in the Monsoon young Ochyoch is depressed. He hasn't done anything drastic yet, but he says he's stopped cutting the whins on his farm because he doesn't want the next tenant to get the benefit of it.

Three out of the last nine years have been disasters in Aberdeenshire, as far as the harvest is concerned, and that's not counting last year when so much wheat was left in the ground. It is a daunting prospect, but it does seem that we may be just too late here to get a good living out of spring rape, and winter wheat and even spring barley has a question mark against it this year.

We have a noble tradition of stockmanship here, and it may be time to reassert that and keep more cattle and sheep. Surely it would make more sense for us to grow winter barley for feed and for bedding, and winter rape for bedding and cash.

The trouble is that the way the EC has organised the economic playing field makes it far more profitable, six out of nine years at least, to grow as much combinable crop as possible, however crazy it may be in relation to our geography.

Phone call fairly dries the wheat

I MADE a valiant effort last week not to bore you with a lament for the harvest. But now, with November upon me and less than half my harvest in, I have to tell it how it is.

It is not good. As I write, it is almost nine weeks since we did any harvesting at all. That must be a record harvest hiatus. Having poured for five weeks, the weather turned changeable. Most days were driech affairs with weak sun, weak drizzle and none of the wind which normally would have dried the crop up.

At last year's yields and values I have £34,000 lying in the fields. Luckily there is absolutely no chance of the yields being anything like last year's and the prices, as you will see if you read on, will be a tiny fraction of last year's. The Farmer's retirement fund is going to take a caning.

My last contractor used to tell me that there was nothing dried the wheat up like somebody else needing the combine. His machines would be stuck on a farm waiting for the farmer to say "GO." He would be dying to get on with earning his twenty pounds an acre, but the farmer would want to delay as long as possible to let the crop dry out and save charges at the mill.

But the minute any of the contractor's other clients needed him, the wheat would turn "wunnerfu dry" and the combining could start immediately without shifting the machines. I suspect the contractor used to get his wife to phone and say there was another farmer ready to go. Either way, it fairly dried the wheat.

I saw a similar phenomenon on the day last week on which our wheat seemed to be nearly dry. I took a sample from the standing crop up to Baldy's, to the Mains and to Mossie's meters, and finally convinced myself that it was below thirty percent. That's twice what we like it to be, and these meters are wildly inaccurate until you get down into the mid-twenties. But November was looming even then.

Two more hours of sunshine in a stiff drying wind and my drip-dry harvest was set to restart. In the morning session it had been observed that my sample was a few points less than Mains', but when I went up to instruct him to start, his wheat had "come on tremendous" and he thought he would just do his remaining 18 acres and come down to my 109 acres the next day.

The rain was sheeting off the porch roof the next day, so the Farmer felt a little bruised by his friendly contractor. However, when Mains got his returns back from the co-op, the Farmer was quite reconciled to being shoved back in the queue. After deductions for drying charges, ingo, and a standard quality penalty, they reckoned Mains' wheat was worth £38 a tonne. That is £95 less than we averaged last year.

Bad, you may think. Yes indeed, but far better than has been the average this week.

All around me, my neighbours have panicked and are cutting the stuff at any moistures, and without doing the sums.

The co-op have though, and they make grim reading. The average stuff they are getting in is of poor quality, and at 40 percent moisture it is leaving the member with £21 a tonne. But, of course, they're not counting little details like combining costs, for which I'd have to count £10 a tonne and haulage, which (at these moistures) will be about £7 per dry tonne.

So I am bid an effective £4 a tonne. That will leave quite a hole in the cash flow compared to last year's equivalent of fully £120.

All that figuring is on the basis of 40 percent moisture, but the co-op have been taking it in at more than that. There has been plenty at 43 percent which is break-even and the record is 53 percent. I don't know how you'd do the sum but at that level the farmer must be owe the co-op a lot of money and have to pay his combine and transport as well.

It's a horror story. But some stock farmers may feel they have to go for it, just to get some straw to bed their beasts through the winter.

Of course, Mossie is still full of optimism. He's been doing a wee bit more every now and again, just to keep the steamer going. He's getting well over two tonnes of wheat and, with his own drying facilities, he's not in the same ball park as Mains and me.

Crookie's in better fettle now too. He's got half his potatoes up in reasonable order, but no harvesting done. The Red Rooster has gone missing, but I saw him swathing a field of the greenest spring rape I've ever seen. He'll definitely not get that dry this year whatever happens to the weather. And poor Young Ochyoch has cut some of the £4 a tonne stuff.

Farmers as a whole have shouted 'wolf' too often, so that, though there is a lot of groaning going on, no one believes that there is much wrong.

But I don't cry 'wolf'. I have always said we were lucky to be doing what we were doing, and that we would struggle through if they'd leave us alone.

But this is on its way to a real disaster for Aberdeenshire. If you've the money with which to buy this is going to be the 'time of opportunity' alright.

Yes, it's "tricky times ahead". I've looked at wrapping and ammonia treating my wheat, and feeding it to the cattle, but at about £6 a bale to do the job I think I'm better to buy the abundant first-class silage that's on the market, and gamble that some week soon there'll be a three days of strong dry wind from the south.

Amazingly there is still a chance for me. Not even the rape has started to sprout and all the wheat is clean and still standing. At £4 a tonne it isn't a big gamble.

My great escape of harvest

A WEEK is a long time in farming.

A week ago I was just about ready to try Mossie's bungie jumping service. And now I am on a high. The salvage is finished. The 1993 harvest on the little farm on the hill is very bad but not a disaster.

I would not have thought it possible so late in the year. You would expect to get the odd hour or two after a couple of days stiff wind from the west and yet, without a breath of wind, our drip dry harvest got going on Monday and by Saturday night we were down at the Salmon celebrating the "Winter" as we used to call "Harvest Home".

"I tell't ye this would be a good week. Aabody panics and cuts their stuff too wet but if you just get aathing ready to GO! You'll aye get it dry eventually." Fair enough but Mossie has been saying that for the last nine weeks in which there was not one grain harvested at Little Ardo. I suppose if we had waited till April to get his fine week he'd have said " I tell't ye we'd get a fine week if we just had patience."

Crookie was there too, surprisingly enough, for this new wife has fairly been winning the struggle against his old batchelor ways. But his daughter, the beautiful Mhairi, has proved a powerful ally. By eight o'clock on Sunday night, the bairn was still yelling, and the suggestion that a run in the car might just do the trick was graciously accepted.

It worked too. The discussion group were amazed when in walked the brave and proud hero swinging what appeared to the older among us to be a shopping basket. The younger members recognised it as a rather natty carry-cot, with an angel asleep in it.

For one who married latish, Crookie has taken very well to parenthood and adapted traditional roles to modern living.

Any suggestion that he would put the angel down in a corner was met with threats of tantrums. This lady is definitely a swinger. But Crookie had the answer. In no time he had de-

veloped a pose, leaning against the bar with his pint in his drinking hand, he swung the carrycot gently with what would otherwise have been his free hand.

It was all done so naturally that we were able to get on with assessing what had been, for me at least, the great escape of harvest.

Mains having had his first cutting of wheat valued by the miller at £38 a tonne decided to cut the last of his and crimp, treat and feed it to his own cattle.

That really wasn't an option for me. I had six times as much wheat and half as many cattle, so I was ecstatic when we got going on Tuesday.

But where do you start when you are expecting to get but a few hours of cutting and you've 109 acres to go? The wheat was the highest value crop by far but we wanted the rape out of the way to let us get next year's wheat sown.

So we cut two ten-acre fields of rape leaving the tramped ends which would just have clogged the machine.

Wednesday was fair again. Not fine, but not raining and, a most unusual feature in these parts, there was no dew, so we managed twenty-nine acres of wheat.

But now came the really Tricky Times. My floater having queued for seven hours to unload at the grain store refused to take any more. It was quite uneconomic for him to pay a man to wait about till half past ten at night. He would take a load first thing but after that he couldn't help.

Having got half my wheat and having no reason to think it any drier than the average of about 35 percent I was faced with the prospect of around eighty tonnes of the stuff rotting in the heap. Tricky Times were here. There was no point in cutting any more wheat to rot.

But on Thursday we had a good day. Aberdeen Grain's Angel of Mercy, Sheila by name, managed to fix me up with a twenty tonner who wasn't too busy for queueing. He managed two loads. And, finishing too late to get a pint, we cut the rest of the rape.

Suddenly it began to look as though we could make it.

The wheat had not heated and, though it had a pathetic specific weight of 58 kilos per hecto-litre (whatever that is it is not good), it was a crackling 25.6 percent moisture. So it wouldn't go far wrong in the heap for a few days.

The rape turned out to be 18 percent so it would be worth something after all. Only thirty-six acres of wheat to go.

On Friday we cut 22 acres of wheat and that seemed even drier. But better than that there appeared to be a crop. It looked like three tonnes of wet grain, but time will tell. I had a fair day of it including filling four lorries as well as carting off from the furthest field.

I also lost my cart, an alarming door I never want to go through again. What happens is, when you tip your load it just keeps on going up and when the point of balance gets behind the back wheels over she goes.

And, with the very last load, I modified the tractor door as I passed the piggery with it flapping open in the manner of a youthful poseur. When I think how nasty I have been to the Wasting Asset when I've seen him driving like that, I am almost ashamed.

On Saturday we had our first heavy dew of the week. However we started in moderate conditions at two and finished just as the first light rain of the week turned to the first downpour.

By next week I'll have a better idea how it has worked out but this will surely be the week when the net worth of the Farmer made its most heroic recovery.

All heading for a mega hangover

THE BOYS are gearing up for the annual pilgrimage to Smithfield.

Mossie is again organising the invasion of the capital. "It's the worst hairst we've ever had, and aabody's gaun tae Smithfield tae celebrate."

Now, it's a funny thing that. Because when the minister wanted to have a 'Harvest Home', Mossie was furious. "Harvest Home, Harvest Home? What harvest home? My harvest's nae hame yet, and neither is onybody else's aboot here. Why should I give thanks for the worst hairst we've ever had, even afore we've even had it?"

But Smithfield is different. Smithfield is a pose. Going to London with the lads is a protest against middle age. It is a demonstration that those who have long since ceased to be batchelors, and were probably never very gay, can still set off for the bright lights and make themselves ill with enjoyment.

Last year, you may recall, in order to relieve that boredom of floating round Earl's Court on a river of liquid hospitality, we decided to go to one of those fancy car auctions. The sellers there where those who thought they had more money than sense, but had discovered they hadn't as much sense as they thought. It was there that I tried to swat a tattie moth and found myself the proud owner of the two year old Jaggie.

The success of that sale is so well renowned that we are being offered a trip round a factory to see how the six figure combines are made. If they are having a roup I will not go unless my hands are firmly tied behind my back. As far as I'm concerned, we are going to see how they make the machines we can no longer afford.

Of course, not everybody's going down. Crookie has a far-away look in his eyes every time it's mentioned. But really he has no chance - and quite right too. He had getting on for twenty years of perfect freedom while the rest of us were gallantly serving our apprenticeships as husbands and fathers. He can't expect us to feel sorry for him if, after one year of marriage and with Mhairi only two months old, he has to stay at home.

He can expect to be indentured for the full five years, and then he will probably find that he'll get back to Smithfield.

Mind you, at first the wife will probably want to come too. This phase is undoubtedly cheaper but, we in the discussion group agree, a couple of years of that is ideal. Then, just about the turn of the century, the wife will get fed up of the annual pilgrimage, and it should be back to the mega-hangovers for which Smithfield was invented.

Potions is not getting to Smithfield either, of course. Being a chemist, and with the trade building up nicely to Christmas, he has to stay at home and help his good lady to mind the store. He'd much rather be away with the lads, because Potions is a frustrated farmer. He has it made, with everybody getting ill and coming streaming into his shop for all kinds of cures paid for by the government, and yet he would be a farmer.

That works very well as far as I'm concerned, because he is ever eager to come down to Little Ardo to play at farms. If there is a loose-box to be mucked out, or a hundred-weight of silage netting to be cut off the muckspreader, all I have to do is lift the phone and the chemist will discard his pestle, put on his boilersuit and his nicky-tams, and get stuck in. But I fear that this disastrous harvest may indeed be a "Time of Opportunity" as

72

Mossie will keep putting it. Potions is dying to get a farm, and after this growing season all his pals are queueing up to get a chemist's shop. They just cannot understand why a man with a thriving business in a nice warm shop would want to plough and sow and scatter the good seed o'er the land, given the poor performance of The Other Party in keeping His side of that bargain. Potions, having longed for a farm for so long, is spoiled for choice now.

He's not getting this place, though I do quite fancy myself in a white coat. You see the salvage operation was really quite a success.

You will recall that, after nine weeks of almost constant rain, I estimated my wheat to be worth about £4 a tonne after drying charges. Well, things improved greatly and by the time the stuff was in at 26 percent moisture only, and at over 58 pounds bushel weight, I reckon that figure could be up from four to seventy pounds a tonne. And again the yield was not as big a disaster as we had feared. It worked out at over 54 cwts per acre.

But that compares miserably with the 72cwts we got last year. The rape is about 14 cwts against more like 18 last year and, of course, there is five percent more water to dry off this year.

I calculated during the nine weeks of rain, that at last year's prices I had £34,000 worth of combinable crops lying in the fields. It is now possible to make a reasonable estimate of how much of that I was able to salvage. It's not an easy sum, with the complications of quality penalties, and the fact that there is now an acreage payment with the wheat, but it appears that I may have salvaged as much as £18,000 at this year's current prices.

Of course I'm much more than £16,000 down, as the harvesting and drying costs are so much higher, never mind the transport costs of all that water.

No wonder we're off to Smithfield. It is an act of defiance.

November 22, 1993

Bonhomie sparked off by five deer

AS I write, the sun is streaming in at the window of the old farm house. The smoke is rising vertically from the chimneys down in the village, and, in the field at the back of the wood my grandfather planted in 1936, there are no fewer than five roe deer grazing the winter barley.

The cattle are all in bar a few autumn calvers who are tidying up the stubble, the overdraft is back but under control, the Breadwinner is away winning bread, the Wasting Asset has started paying income tax and I am a lucky man. Better than that, I know it.

Those five deer were the spark which set off my bonhomie this morning. We are often told that wildlife is under threat from modernisation, from monoculture and from pesticides. No doubt it is in many places, but the evidence of my own eyes over fifty years on Ardo's hill is that wildlife is winning here.

There is far more of it, and as far as I can judge, there is more diversity too. I never saw

a hawk, a fox or a magpie when I was a boy and now they proliferate. They live off wildlife and are proof that there is plenty of it about.

We even had an osprey here. It arrived some ten years ago and nested in the historic woods of Gight until some do-gooder, conserving naturalist, cut down the tree it nested in on the grounds that it was a non-indigenous tree, whatever that is.

That was a bad day for the Osprey, but with me all is well. And yet I nearly threw it all away on Sunday at the discussion group meeting at the Salmon Inn.

It really has been a bitch of a year, and Mossie was holding court on just how bad. Each in turn confessed to having yields as big as they thought they could get away with. They were not high - most people claiming to have got around half their usual yields for spring rape and wheat.

Now, Mossie made an uncharacteristic tactical mistake. He let everyone else say what

74

their yields of wheat were. No one had got two tonnes to the acre. There only being me left to declare, he told them all, and with a devil may care sweep of the arm: "We had two tonnes fourteen - an absolute disaster."

The secret this year was to keep the crop standing, and this he had done with the aid of his own personal cocktail of environmenticides. But what he had forgotten was that he had been acting as my crops adviser. I too had applied the cocktail. I too had averaged two tonnes fourteen. It needed only the merest exaggeration to put me into the lead with, "Jist hardly two tonnes fifteen".

I would not have enjoyed my moment of triumph had I seen its full implications.

Mossie was soon onto next year's rape. He had just finished spraying his winter crop. Bold as brass, I asked the great man what I was to apply to mine.

"Oh na, na." He says. "You're better than me at growin crops noo, so we'll see how you get on withoot my advice."

It was a bad moment. I know very well that this little farm can be profitable, even in a bad year, but only if everything is done right. My track record shows clearly that I need some help in that department. And here was my honorary consultant handing in his cards.

Of course, the solution was obvious, if a bit embarrassing. I had forgotten that the croft park had been remeasured and was fifteen acres rather than thirteen, and so that put my yield down to two tonnes thirteen. Still second best, but not as good as the master.

So pleased was he that at the end of the evening he scribbled out a ticket and said, "Get that on your rape the morn, and then destroy that ticket."

Mossie has a reputation for sound man-management, but it is his woman management that never ceases to astound.

On Sunday the discussion group got off to an early start. There was a lot to discuss, with the end of harvest near for all but the most backward members.

By four o'clock some of us were starting to look anxiously at the clock, and by five it was clear that a fair night was in prospect. At least we would get away home at half past five because the saintly woman who married Mossie all those years ago had something special for his tea.

At six he noticed the time and said, "Oh, and I'll need a Mars bar for the wife." Soon it was two more Mars bars for the wife, who must be getting very angry as her special supper spoiled. By seven o'clock Mossie was nursing his umpteenth pint and a double handful of Mars bars.

The phone rang. It had to be a wife, for he was not the only one with supper to go to. It was Mrs Moss.

You don't often get our man looking uncomfortable, but he was uneasy.

We watched and tried to listen.

It didn't sound like a row. Soothing and even loving words seemed to be coming down the phone. Gradually Mossie relaxed. "She's put my supper in the oven, and she disna think I should drive hame, so she's comin for me. But she canna come till eight o'clock. He, heeee!"

He picked up the fourteen Mars bars and turned to the barmaid. "I dinna need all this sweeties noo. Can you tak them back and gie's a double gin and orange for them?"

What a woman! She even had the decency to arrive nearly an hour late - and took a row for it. I know he'd have bought her a drink, but then again, she was driving.

Big Hamish becomes a blue blood

I TOLD you about Big Hamish buying the estate down by the coast, and how it enabled him to realise his life's ambition to join the the 1000-acre club.

But what I didn't tell you was that, in buying the place, Hamish has become part of the aristocracy. For it includes the historic castle of Slains, and Hamish is now the Baron of Slains. The baronial courts don't function much in Scotland these days, but it does rather make the blood curdle to think of the Big Baron Hamish dispensing justice (or otherwise), as he saw fit, and with the power of life and death over all us peasant farmers.

Hamish is also impressed. He told me the other day that he cut himself shaving, "And de ye ken this, Charlie?" he said, "The bleed ran blue."

That could well be, and they do say that on quiet nights you can see a kilted figure parading

77

the ramparts of Slains Castle. Some people think it is a large ghost but I have another theory. It is the Baron of Slains himself, come to survey his lands, or to gaze out across the sea for raiders, against which his predecessors built the great fort.

I expect this year the Baron looked mostly to the sea, for, with the horrendously wet summer, the sight to landward was not appetising - at least not to a farmer's eyes.

Indeed, so wet has it been that the laird might have had difficulty in knowing whether he was looking out to sea or not.

When Hamish took over the baronial acres, they were in somewhat undistinguished crops. Hamish's real test will come when he gets going with all his expensive plant and harvests the first of his own crops.

But still, a good harvest this year would have been a nice bonus.

There was no such chance at the Barony. With the water table several feet above ground level in places, one of the main hazards standing between Hamish and a bounteous harvest, were the ducks.

His lands lie close to several bird sanctuaries and there were literally thousands of ducks swimming around the flooded fields and ducking for the heads of sodden grain. It was very frustrating for the big man. "If only I could keep them damned ducks aff and give it a chance to dry, I could have a crop yet."

You remember how, when oil seed rape was grown for tonnage rather than for acreage, we used to put our old machinery and scrapped cars in the rape fields to scare off the pigeons? Well, Hamish is trying the same with the ducks. He's looking for as many scrap boats as he can get to moor them in his fields as scare-ducks.

I can't see it working, but it will look well from the road.

Of course, some of the lads can't understand what Big Hamish wants with such a well-watered place.

I can though. And it's not just the being a baron.

For Slains is famous the world over as the inspiration for Bram Stoker's earth-shattering and spine-tingling horror novel, Dracula. It is absolutely ideal for a Dracula theme-park. There will be diversification grants available to the baron, and it is a very exciting subject.

The theme park will be educational too, because Dracula did exist, and he was a most interesting character. He liked

78

to cut people up, force them to eat one another, and enjoyed nothing more than a good meal surrounded by corpses and near corpses impaled on wooden stakes. That earned him his other name, Vlad the Impaler.

I told the Red Rooster about the scope Big Hamish has given himself by buying the barony but he is unimpressed. "Well, you'd better be richt. For I canna see that Dracula could have thought of a worse torture for onybody than fairmin that swamp."

I despair. Some folk have no imagination.

Meanwhile, the times of opportunity unfold. The combination of poor harvest and setaside have produced an acute shortage of straw. Anyone who managed to get any decent stuff surplus to requirements, is on a good thing.

Poor quality straw baled in only a light rain is making eight pounds a bale, and it has been a lifeline to young Ochyoch. He has had a better harvest than many, but with being newly into the place he needed it much more than most. So the straw has produced anything up to eighty pounds an acre of a bonus.

Yes it's times of opportunity, all right. Now is the time for us to squeeze some of their profits out of the dairymen.

And what about the young laird. He's the only other blue blood in the discussion group and he is a most progressive fellow. He is so progressive and environmentally friendly that he had the central heating system in his stately home converted to straw-burning. And where has that got him? With the price of straw through the roof he can't afford to put the heating on, so he comes down to the Salmon Inn just for the heat. And with so much water in the straw this year, it puts out black reek which has been reported to the environmental health.

So the young laird is converting back to oil. Times of opportunity for the central heating people.

Now, the young laird is progressive in many ways, but not with women. He's forty already - and still single. We were all agog, therefore, when we heard he'd got a rather shapely au-pair land girl to help out on the farm.

She put him in his place too. The first day, a typical Indian winter day in November, he showed her the combine with which he was trying to salvage the spring rape. "I see. Also een France we do eet, but we do eet in de summer."

79

Finding new truths on Sod's law

OH! THE things you see when you haven't got a gun. It's always the same. Take a stroll through the cows in the morning and you'll put up half a dozen pheasants and a brown hare that would make a suppy grand soup. But if you decide to go home for the gun to get something for the pot, you'll stroll alone through the Howe.

That is Sod's Law of Blood Sports. And I believe that the boys and I have found out new truths about it. We are excited about our discovery, and are not sure whether the final results should be published in *Lancet* or *Nature*, so I thought I'd try you with the preliminary findings.

On Saturday we had our annual shoot over Little Ardo's fertile acres. There have been countless pheasants reared by wild hens this year, despite the weather. There are at least five double-figure coveys of partridges. We have rather too many rabbits on a farm which has never had a rabbit problem. We haven't a rabbit problem this year, but they all seem to be in the Breadwinner's garden. As ever there are a million pigeons.

We have not fewer than five big roe deer and one little one. I wouldn't want to shoot them, though they must have reached numbers at which shooting is just an alternative to some other death. They cannot all get through the winter. Another I wouldn't shoot is the woodcock I saw in the wood the other day, for that was the first I'd seen on Little Ardo in fifty years here.

Anyway, I told the lads that woodcock were out, and that the deer were to be left to those with rifles. That seemed reasonable, though I knew that no one had a rifle, and a good day's mayhem seemed likely.

It was a big disappointment. We saw one woodcock and we saw four deer. We shot one rabbit - and that was all we had by lunchtime. That was embarrassing.

"You're going through a bad patch," said Mossie over his third large ginny, "but you'd have thocht there would be some grain on this hill for the pheasants. What happened to aa' that stuff you had to leave in the field at hairst time?"

It was Crookie that sparked off our great experiment. Like the nice man he is (nicer than the Rooster and Mossie anyway), he said: "It's aye the same. If you'd've been spraying or spreading muck, there'd of been pheasants aa' ower the place."

It seemed worth a try.

After a jolly lunch and Mossie, the Red Rooster and Crookie were sent to the bottom of the Lang Park to make a drive towards the standing guns.

Those were myself (Digger), Willie the Hunter (Jeep), and Potions the Chemist (ride-on mower).

And, you know, it worked a treat.

As the great armoured corps advanced up the park, game abounded. There were pheasants galore, four hares, and their

much planning, we went out and yoked the Nat to the muckspreader, the Fergie to the sprayer, and the close brush, which was already on the old Fordson Major. In those,

biggest problem was avoiding running-over the partridges.

I shouldn't say this but, after the morning we'd had, some of the troopers weren't too fussy about sitting birds and soon the bag was heavier.

Mind you, at first it wasn't much fun for the standing guns. The birds were so used to ignoring farm machinery that nothing was put up to flight. But after they got the idea, we too were on to a good thing. Instead of their usual action to avoid the standing guns, our hapless prey flew straight over us.

It presented us with new challenges. It is surprisingly difficult to shoot out of the cab of a digger. You are just following the flight of a pheasant over your head when it disappears from your view and the barrel of your gun cracks against the roof of the cab. And accurate shooting from a moving 590 is not easy, especially if you are going across the tramlines.

Indeed, though we did get the bag up to enough for the satisfaction of honour, and to give the lads a brace each to give to people who they knew hated cleaning game, we could not have said the bag was heavy.

And we are conscious that we have not explained Sods Law of Blood Sports. But even if we still don't understand it, at least we know now how to combat it.

While we're on blood sports, I am relieved to be able to tell you that the trip to Smith-field didn't come off. And again, I don't really understand why.

Mossie it was who had everything arranged. We would fly down for three days and two nights. We'd go to visit a combined-harvester assembly plant, and we'd paint the town red.

But then mysteriously he went cold on the idea. It may have had something to do with his pigman leaving, but at any rate he couldn't go.

Now, another of the stars of our last trip to Smithers was the man called Nicol from Keith. He's the one who, you will remember, wanted to get discount off the champagne at a Chinese restaurant in Soho. Getting no satisfaction from the waitress, he asked for, and was refused, an interview with the manager.

But if Nicol from Keith is to take no for an answer, he likes to get it from the head of the mule. "I'll gang and get him," he said and rushed downstairs. He arrived back in no time with the Chinaman under his arm.

Don't let anybody tell you the Chinese have no sense of humour. He was delighted. He even baked a birthday cake for Nicol. We had it for desert. But he didn't get his discount.

Anyway, Nicol from Keith

called off when he heard Mossie wasn't going. He put it like this. "For a trip like that ye need at least two complete idiots."

That was it. We all agreed. The trip was off.

December 13, 1993

Launched on maiden flight

SATURDAY WAS diversification day with the launch of Volume Two of Farmer's Diary. The literati and the glitterati of "Aiberdeen and twal mile roon" met at the Salmon Inn to give a fitting send-off to another attractive maky-on leatherbound collection of these articles and Turnbull's cartoons, reproduced from the *Herald*.

Like all grand social occasions, the scope for ill-will was considerable. There was the business of who to invite, for a start. Who didn't buy a book last time, and so could be left out and damn the consequences?

Whose would be the honour of performing the launching ceremony? That was a tricky one, for we'd an embarrassment of talent. Last time we'd had Jack Sleigh, then Chairman of the Royal Highland and Agricultural Society. He'd bought two books so he would be invited for sure.

And then we felt it was only right and proper that the young laird be asked to launch the book, as the old laird was away in London making megamillions in the City. But then again, Big Hamish is now a blue-blood having bought the famous Barony of Slains and its castle.

Tricky times were here.

Anyway, it was decided that, as Big Hamish had only been an aristocrat for three months, the young laird should do it.

Again, it was planned more as an unveiling than a launching. Last year Jack Sleigh had said a few kind words about the Farmer and then lifted the empty feed bag off the pile of books. But the young laird did it differently.

His kind words were fewer and, I thought, less kind than Mr Sleigh's had been. He whipped the black plastic bale-wrap off and grabbed a precious volume. "I hereby, and with much pleasure launch this book," he said. Then, winding himself up like a baseball pitcher, he launched the book across the bar.

Who knows the thought processes of the aristocracy? It's well understood that they are so bred down, that they may think anything. But it was as though the young laird had some twisted idea of performing the traditional launch of a ship.

There, they throw a perfectly good bottle of champagne at it.

What the young laird did was just the reverse. He threw the book at the row of bottles behind the bar. The book's maiden flight carried it clattering in amongst the expensive liquors and malt whiskies, where it knocked a bottle of ten year old Macallan right off the shelf. Amid thunderous applause from the intelligentsia of Methlick, the bottle was caught, inches from the ground by Crookie, the grain baron who once fielded in the slips for Fisherford school second eleven.

Although the book is published here, that has all been done by the Breadwinner who has taught herself desk-top publishing in her spare time. So I hadn't remembered what was in Volume Two. I was favourably impressed. There is the story of Old Drumlie shooting the bairns football, and my father selling the homing pigeons time after time; he could afford to sell cheap because they just flew home again. And there is the farm walk from which a neighbour went home wearing one natty Italian slip-on and one tattie-crisp packet.

Then there is the story about Mossie taking the barbecue pig to the slaughterhouse in a poke in the front of the car. The piggie got out and impressed our man with its intelligent interest in what was in the ashtrays and in his pockets, how it put its feet up on the dashboard and looked out at the world going bye, and how it licked him on the cheek. By the time he reached the slaughterhouse, Mossie couldn't stand it. He took the pig home and got another one, making sure not to catch the substitute's eye.

At the launch party we had turkeys from the Mains and salmon from the Ythan, baked tatties from the Rooster's shed, and green vegetables from Marks and Spencers. But the centre-piece was again a great big porker spit-roasted whole on Mossie's mobile, the converted rotaspreader.

Willie the Hunter has made a wooden stretcher to bear the feast to the multitude. When Willie and Mossie had the pig decanted, apple in its mouth, and ready to go, I opined, in a learned sort of way, that apart from the fact that the stretcher needed painting, the scene reminded me of a feast painted by the sixteenth century Dutch master Bruegel.

Mossie wasn't sure about that though. "Oh aye", he said a little uncertainly. "Would we get him to paint the stretcher, like?"

There was a suggestion that Mains, who is a most willing piper, should pipe the feast in. Unfortunately I had forgotten to tell him and he'd come without the pipes.

"Far better withoot them," said the Red Rooster. "They mak an awfu din in a wee place like this. We aa ken whit they soun like and we aa ken 'Scotland the Brave'. Mains you lead the way and mak on yer playin and that'll dae fine."

And so it was. Mains solemnly lead the procession, blowing away at a piece of kindling wood and pumping at a cushion he held under his elbow. We all hummed 'Scotland the Brave' through our noses, while Mossie and Willie the Hunter bore in the feast.

The party started at 6.30, and by half past midnight Volume Two was well and truly launched. The pork crackling was the most delicious I've ever tasted and it was a most jolly, if jolly expensive, do.

We didn't sell many books, though. There are plenty left.

Cattle prefer steading to snow

I HAVE always believed, been brought up thinking any other belief to be immoral, that all races are intellectually equal. By that I mean that if babes from Borneo are given the same chances, they will reach the same level of attainment as the British, French, or even the Irish.

I stick to that view as far as people are concerned - but it is definitely not so with cows. That much was proved to me on Friday.

That was the day we had the biggest fall of snow so far this year. I awoke feeling that there had been a change in the weather. When I looked out, I saw that I was right. It had been a hard night when I sniffed the air at half past ten. Now, the air was full of huge wet snowflakes the volume of ping pong balls. There was quite a breeze, but there was no chance of this stuff drifting. It lay in a soggy carpet to a depth of six inches and rising.

It was our second major fall this winter and usually we don't expect snow till about the new year. Having been a record year for rain and cloud surely it isn't going to be a record year for snow too.

But that is getting away from the point. As I was sitting down to my breakfast I heard the sound the stockman hates the most. There was a cow bellowing and it was too near to be where it should be. A quick check showed that the close was full of cows and more were arriving from the hill.

I was in time to save the Breadwinner's lawn, thank goodness, and though I did have to get them back out of one field of winter barley, it really wasn't hard to recapture them, even without help.

It was just a case of shutting all the gates until they had only one way to go, that being home. So hungry were they that the sight of a North Eastern Farmers feed bag was all that was needed to get them going.

Now here is the interesting point. My herd of fifty cows consists of some thirty-five Hereford-Friesian, a dozen Simmentals, two Shorties and a Blue Grey. And the funny thing is that it was only the Hereford-Friesians that had broken loose.

What had happened was this. The cows are going in and out just now and I had given them access to a new field of stubble. To get there from their shed, they have to squelch down a couple of hundred yards of track, along the Howes maybe six hundred yards and then up through a gate.

Getting home may not seem a severe test of memory, but if you're a Hereford-Friesian it seems to be.

Of course I was cosy in my bed so I didn't see it, but this seems to have been what happened.

When the storm came on, all the ladies were in the new park enjoying a bite of autumn grass. They put their backsides to the wind as always and grazed as long as they could. When the stubble started to disappear, the Simmentals, the Shorties and the Blue Grey, reluctantly put their heads down into the wind, struggled against the blast to the bottom of the field, found the gate, trotted along the Howes and squelched up the track to their warm court.

They all made it home.

But not one of the Hereford-Friesians did. They were driven before the wind to the top of the field. There they stood against the fence, bellowing for better luck and pushing to get to the front, where there would at least be the shelter provided by those at the back. And those at the back had no other thought than to be at the front.

Inevitably, given the strength of the Little Ardo fences, the paling gave way about daybreak and they all poured out onto the road and high-tailed it for the steading.

But isn't it strange that they should behave so differently according to breed?

When I started to write this, I was going to point out that this must show a cerebral weakness in either the Hereford or the Friesian breeds, for they were all brought up under the same regime here at Little Ardo. I seemed to be forced into the politically quite wrong conclusion. I might have been accused of being a breedist.

But then I remembered they were not all treated the same. There is one important difference in the way these animals were brought up. The stupid Hereford-Friesians were bucket reared from a batch I bought in from England, whereas all the Simmentals, the Blue Grey and the Shorties, were suckled. Breast is best you see. My cows are politically correct.

And I'll tell you another thing about my cows. They're not getting back to that stubble field.

And finally, I'm sorry I haven't been keeping you up to date with Mossie's sunflowers. The last time we were on the subject, he had confounded everyone by growing sunflowers in the wettest field on Mossside in the wettest year there has been since Noah. He had annoyed us even further by finding a market for these at a pound a piece or £25,000 an acre.

We were left with some consolations, mind. He had only sold a big fraction at that and he'd never harvest the rest.

Well, I have bad news for all his friends. Mossie did manage to harvest the happy faces. When he got fed up of buying anti-freeze for them in November, he got in a Mega and slashed them down. There wasn't enough to fill the drier so he had to tray-dry them in the oven. Mrs Moss said it was alright as long as it was finished in time to get the turkey on.

In the end he got seven cwts to the acre and now has enough seed to sow half of Aberdeenshire. And he's claiming the EC acreage subsidy of £240 an acre.

"Oh," he says, without a trace of a smile, "but you need the subsidy."

89

Streaker in the night

IT IS good to know that the days of male chauvinism are not quite dead, and even better to know that we, in Methlick, are one of its last bastions. I had this confirmed last week at the Farmers' Ball. That is the dinner and dance which the dwindling number of farmers organise for the growing numbers of insurance brokers, bankers, teachers and oilmen who inhabit the village.

It is a sort of coming together of two cultures. That is to say ours and that of the entire rest of the world. We do our best to explain ours to the newcomers. I expect he was doing that when the president, young Auchnie, in welcoming the guests, did a bit of advertising on behalf of one of his friends who has decided that the time has come for a serious wife-hunt.

"He's nae carin if she's nae that bonny. He's nae fussy if she canna cook. But it would be handy if she knew how to redd a drain and take oot a hole for a strainer post. So if ye hear o' a girl like that gaun spare

just let Wullie ken. And with no more ado I call on the Reverend Haddow to say grace."

And I do my best to coach my rough friends in the sophisticated ways of the world, for I lived for a decade in Glasgow and three years in Kenya where I learned a thing or two. I try to stop them showing themselves up in front of all the incomers.

When Mossie had said about how the wine would need to be 'richt cauld', I explained to him that these folk only liked the white wine cold, and that the red should be served at room temperature. "Well, in the Beaton Hall in December that is cauld," he replied, hurt and resentful.

I thought he had understood though, and when he was going round with the two bottles and asking in his best English voice "red or white?" I thought to show off our savoir faire.

"Is it chambre, Mossie?" I asked a little too loudly and put my hand knowingly on the bottle of red. Mossie looked startled, examined the bottle carefully and said, "Na, na. It's Beaujolais."

He fairly knows how to shut me up though. "I hear there's word o' a streaker on the head o' the hill," he said.

Well there isn't, of course, but as usual where there is smoke there is at least some fire.

You see, I have followed in a tradition which has existed in my family for at least four generations. The male members have always liked to go outside at night for a few lungfuls of the evening air. It is part weather-forecasting device, part sensuous communication with the elements, and part escape from female company (in the case of those long past the need for tact), or in my case, the television.

There is another element to my story. I generate enough heat to power a small town, and oftentimes I cannot sleep for the heat I produce.

Now the Breadwinner is a consumer of heat. She can drain a hot water bottle of all its heat in half an hour and she needs a hundredweight of bedclothes just to stave off frostbite. She chases me round the bed in search of my heat and is warmed when she catches me.

But so am I. My main method of escape is to sleep on top of the covers, because I know she dare not follow me out into the night air. Sometimes I fool her. When she has pursued me so that I am hanging onto my side of the bed by my teeth and my toes, I sneak out and round to her side. It takes her a while to get her heat-seeking device reorientated and I get a while's peace to cool.

Now, there are times when I rise in the night and go outside for a sniff of the air. It has a keenness then, and the dew on the grass in front of the house is delicious under hot feet.

But there was eight inches of snow on the grass when I rose the other night. You could have fried an egg on my feet and soon I was outside in my cutty sark and melting the snow. It was a windless night. The stars twinkled down on me, and I twinkled back at them.

We never used to lock the doors, and we've no reason to think we need to now. It's just all the publicity and advancing years that have made us nervous. To save the Breadwinner's precious heat, I pulled the door shut. One click of the Yale and I was locked out.

Panic. I could see the headlines: "Methlick streaker caught." What would my ancestors think?

It is amazing how quickly

'nice and cool' turns to 'bloody freezing' when your retreat is cut off.

Would I throw stones at her window? But where do you get stones in eight inches of snow. And anyway, the Breadwinner sleeps like she's been hit by a very cold train.

What is the Guinness record for surviving in eight inches of snow wearing only a cutty sark? Could I make it to the barn and survive there in the straw till morning. What would they say when the cutty sark emerged from the barn in the morning?

All this swept before my panicking eyes. I longed for a share of the Breadwinner's hundredweight of bedclothes. *Methlick Farmer freezes to death. Widow praises the General Accident Mutual Insurance Fund as she sails for the Caribbean.*

In the vain hopes that no one would see, and that the woman who never forgets to do anything would have forgotten to lock the back door, I twinkled round to the door which leads out to the yard, or in to wonderful heat, depending on which way you are facing.

I got one out of two. The door was open - but Mossie found out and I'm damned sure I didn't tell him.

92

So it's all her fault really

I HAVE long realised that organisation is one of the keys to success on the farm. It is possible to spend ages casting around the farm for tools. If you don't know where the socket set is you can lose the best of the day and all of your humour, looking for it. And there is nothing worse than getting the cattle in for worming and, with the staff expensively hired all poised for action, be stuck for a syringe. There is nothing worse than workers standing about while you run to the vet for more wormer.

But realising what needs to be done is seldom the mother of the deed. Mostly I keep things near to the place where I last used them.

That works surprisingly well when you are young and your memory isn't flustered by age. But when memory dims or when the person who used it last is from home, the peak of efficiency with which I would like to run the place becomes a distant prospect.

The waste this causes is bad enough, but the conflict it causes with the Breadwinner is something else.

It's all her fault really. You see she not only has a perfect memory for where she left everything, but she has a place for everything and replaces what she uses immediately. When she sets off for her job in the toon it is just too tempting for me.

If I can't find one of my hammers, I know where to find one. She keeps the house hammer under the stairs along with her set of screwdrivers and her excellent pliers. And should I need a spade, or a rake or a garden graip, I know they will be in the garden shed.

As soon as the Breadwinner is off to do her ten hours of work, I effectively annex her domaine.

It works very well until I start applying my working practices to her implements. It isn't too bad if I mislay garden tools or those from under the stair. Those misdemeanours only lead to sulking, sarcastic comments and small forfeits

like having to wash her car.

But hell hath no fury like that of the woman who is all set to do the washing-up when she discovers that her Squeezy has all been used as frost-proofing for the latest load of readymix. That happened last week. After years of doing a wee bit more any time there was another few quid between me and the current overdraft limit, I finally achieved, in September, what I set out to do in 1973. We now have tar or concrete over the fifteen hundred yards or so of our private roads.

Now, you'd expect a wife to share in the joy of such an achievement. After all she complained hard enough about it before it was finished. And, to be fair, she was doing her best to sound enthusiastic.

Then she reached for the Squeezy. This time I had returned the carton but it was empty. How she knew it was me I do not know. It must have been blind prejudice, but any Brownie points I might have thought I had earned were a-wayyyy.

Of course things aren't as bad nowadays as they were when we showed our pedigree cattle. That always seemed to involve things of which we run out. They were washed in Lux and I always knew where to get some of that. The dangleberries had to be cut off and a good pair of kitchen shears were as good as any for that. Then there was a suppy polish for their hooves or three-in-one oil for their coats, and there was no place like the wash-house for a nice clean scrubbing brush and bucket.

Mind you, if we had still had the show cattle I dare say one of the hair-driers would have been working and that would have saved this latest row.

We had another late calf from one of the old bangers I bought last back end to make up the numbers for the beef-cow quotas. It was a poor thing and probably would have died even if she had chosen to have it inside instead of behind a dyke on a snowy night.

Nevertheless, and even when you know quite well that there is no hope, you have to try. So we took her in...soaking.

The first job was to get her dry and for that what better than one of these things that grate so on the nerves as they whine and blow hot air at the bulls? But one didn't have a plug and the other didn't seem to know what to do with one. So I borrowed the Breadwinner's. And four hot-water bottles - and the extension cable so that I could fix up the hot lamp.

The Herald would never print what she called me the next day when she was needing all her time to get her hair dried and off to work the next morning. And she seemed not at all impressed at the speed with which I rushed out to the shed, found the drier in the straw and brought it back with hardly any muck on it at all.

I can see that I am not entirely blameless in all this, but what am I to do about her attitude now? The other day we had some people to a magnificent roast of Limousin-cross-AA heifer. But where was the carving knife? For once it wasn't me. I have never had occasion to carve anything on the farm and I could never forget an act of bravery like borrowing the carving knife.

I don't mind being accused of having taken what I have taken but it is a bit thick when you are blamed for having taken what you never took.

Tricky decisions to be made

1994 IS off to a flying start. It seems like half an hour since we were looking forward to a jolly evening at the Salmon. We would then go home to see out the old year and welcome those who came with their first feet. Indeed Mossie put a new slant on that old tradition. He had to be carried in feet first. We looked forward to four long days of doing nothing and doing it slowly.

In the event, the days sped past almost unnoticed. Suddenly it is the fifth of the new year as I sit down to fill another page of this farmer's diary. There's little to tell because it is mostly forgot, but I am happy about one thing. Doing it this way economises on the hangovers. I am getting them all over with at once.

I always promise to myself, the Breadwinner, and my heirs that I will try to do things a bit better next year.

But really, I hardly made any mistakes last year.

It's true that my wheat was grown from home-saved seed which showed very low germination. But that mistake was made in the back end of 1992. I calculated that it wouldn't matter how thinly I sowed the spring rape, as the price would be too low to make the harvest worth bothering about. That was badly wrong too, as rape went to almost twice what I expected. And I believed the vet when he told me it was unusual for a cow to go down a second time with staggers. I should have had her off to the jingo-ring and seven hundred pounds in the bank. Instead, I had to pay the knacker twenty pounds to dispose of her.

All in all, though, the Farmer did a good job in 1993. He didn't panic at harvest time - not even when it was long past harvest time - and all crops were got in fair order and middling quantity. The harvest which was a disaster for many, was no more than a disappointment on Ardo's hill. All spraying was done timeously, and if he did sell one heifer with a passport, on the whole he coped well with the new system of subsidies.

Quite the best piece of farming he did in 1993 was to keep the piggery empty. As the price of weaners came down and down, as fortunes were lost by the nation's pig producers, the Farmer resisted the temptation to fill up the shed, fill up the feed store, and empty the bank account.

Every piggy not bought was money saved in 1993. And on some of those piggies the money saved would have been more than ten pounds. He could have had 1600 piggies losing ten pounds each, but instead had none.

So, all I can do is to resolve to do the same again in 1994, and hope that He who dictates the weather does His part of the job a little better.

It's not that all is well on the farm. As we enter the new year, the winter wheat we sowed in ley is looking very well, but the stuff that followed the spring rape hasn't even got through the ground yet. Indeed, I'm not even sure that it is trying.

The winter barley is a show, but the winter rape is looking very timid indeed. It should be thick enough to create its own micro-climate, to protect the little plants from the worst of the weather, but it is far from that. Each little plant has a clear six inches of its own space and pretty cold it looks too. However they are all there so they should flourish when spring comes again to Aberdeenshire.

Mind you, there are some tricky decisions to be made in 1994. I face one every day: to bed the cattle or not to bed the cattle, that is one of the questions.

At first sight that doesn't look a difficult one. We have plenty of good straw, so why not give them a nice cosy winter? Well, the trouble is that dry straw is scarce. Even wet straw, stored outside, has been selling at over six pounds a bale and muck, rotted outside, has been making over five pounds. What, therefore, must my nice, dry, inside stored, winter-barley straw be worth? It cannot be less than ten pounds a bale.

So how can I waste money putting stuff like that in amongst cow's feet? They'll even go and eat it, and that's a worse waste still. You can buy silage for six pounds a bale, and when silage is so much more nutritious than straw, you can't have them filling up on that. It makes no sense feeding cattle on a high fibre diet, when you could be fattening them for less money.

We do have a number of rape-straw bales, and we are using those up, but it really is heart-breaking putting ten pound a bale straw in amongst the muck.

This is the fourth year in a row that silage has been plentiful about here, and I've ploughed up the field that would have given me silage in 1994. The plan is to produce as much subsidised grain as possible, and buy in silage. If the straw can be given as a clean swap for silage, that must be right.

Of course, things may be quite different next year. But, in the meantime, I must get some of that straw on the market.

I missed a chance the other day at the Field Engineering Services' clay pigeon shoot and barbecue. There were many farmers there with more money than straw, and I was geared up for a few private deals.

Getting down to basics

THE BOYS in the discussion group have been giving the government a hard time of it, over it's policy of Back to Basics. I suppose we're no different from any other non-committed group in the things we have been saying about the moral debate which is sweeping the country.

Like everybody else, we are a bit bemused. We can believe that it is more than just a case of them telling us to do what we always knew we should, while they carry on doing what we always knew they did, it's just that it doesn't seem like it.

And I'm afraid the lads are a bit cynical.

Big Hamish says they are intending to fight the next election on the slogan, "Life is better under the Conservatives".

And Peter, the man who sold me my digger and is still laughing about it with his banker, says it is a fiendish plot. The Tories, having decided to blame all the ills of society on those wicked single parents, are hell-bent on creating as many single mothers as they can.

But it is not basic morality that the boys are most annoyed about. We agree with the position that Major seems now to be adopting, that there are more important basics that they need to get back to.

And the basics we want more emphasis on are the three Rs - especially the third (Rithmetic). We want them to learn to count. The policy of reducing the surpluses of grain and oilseeds is based on a planned reduction in the area under cultivation. And yet it has emerged that the Government's statisticians had only the vaguest idea of what acreage there was to start with.

As the Red Rooster put it, "There's thoosands o' them, in their fine warm offices, and they hinna a clue what they're daein." It's hard to argue with that. At first they told some of us we'd have to set aside an extra sixteen percent of our arable because we'd sown that much more than expected. Then it appeared that it would only be 5.4 percent extra set-aside, and now all are agreed that we hardly need to increase set-aside at all.

The buzzword for all this confusion is the "arable overshoot." But we don't see it that way at all. They underestimated the basic area. We couldn't possibly overshoot. We were told to set aside 15 percent, and the correctly filled up IACS form made damned sure we did. We didn't overshoot anything.

The cases of people like me were too well known. In the previous year I made an arithmetical error which awarded me a few hundred pounds in extra grant. It was the sort of mistake anyone could have made. To be exact, I added 2.7 hectare and 2.2 hectares and got 5.9 hectares. Luckily, I had underclaimed some other bits and pieces, but it would have left me distinctly better off. So they deducted my overclaim, and then deducted the same again - so that I would tell all my pals not to risk it.

I did tell them, and the nation's farmers were so scared they could not possibly have overshot, however hard they might have tried, and however unnatural honesty in matters of grant might be to them.

So how did the Rithmetic go so wrong?

There are lots of reasons, each understood by someone, but none understood by all. Mossie says it's because of

100

some idiots not knowing whether wheat claimed as forage in the IACS forms should be counted as wheat or as forage in the NON-LFA land. I should have thought the confused should be forgiven there.

But surely the blunder was in using the annual returns to calculate the base area.

It seems to be accepted that those returns are not done with any great care anyway, but there is a far worse aspect of the decision to use the census to form a base for set-aside.

Despite the statutory obligation to do so, in the region of one in seven farmers have not been making an annual return. That was surely remiss of them, but the infuriating thing is that the authorities seem to have been doing nothing about it. The boys in the Salmon Inn Discussion Group want the government to know that they are not going to fill in any more of their forms. Of course, we agree the Government should get the information but, if they are not going to enforce collection, the information is at best useless - and in this case was acutely damaging to our interests.

A bright child doing statistics at school could have told them that they would get nonsense if they used the area of turnips to calculate the area of golf courses. But as far as we can see, they did all their negotiations with Europe on the basis of figures everybody knew were wrong.

What brought the huge discrepancy to light was the new system of support for farmers. When they were told they'd get up to £240 an acre for declaring their crops, there were very few who did not comply. When they were told it would cost them double if they overclaimed, they made very sure they were accurate. You get a different response if you tell farmers to do something for nothing, than if you offer to pay them a king's ransom to do it, and fine them for inaccuracy.

As you can see, we were taking life more seriously than sometimes at the Salmon on Sunday.

Well, most of us were. Willie the Hunter is less interested in LFAs, IACS, and CCDs than the rest of us, and he wasn't missed from the discussion. Eventually Mossie felt a tugging on his trouser leg. Looking down he was astonished to see Willie lying flat on his back.

"What's the dae wi ye Willie?" says Mossie. "I'm on a low," said the Hunter.

January 24, 1994

Letting go with both barrels

IT'S ALL right for the Red Rooster and Mossie. Being in the A team they have no problem filling up the dark days of winter. Even before Mossie converted the old Rotaspreader into a barbecue and got going in catering, they were always partying.

Just now it's shoots. They are out every second day knocking six bells out of mother nature's finest gifts and doing their best to put new life into the trade for malting barley.

Only having half a day's shooting of my own, I can't get into their social whirl because I can't take my turn as host.

Mind you, I'm glad they didn't invite me to that one last Saturday. It gave me the chance to go to see Huntly disposing of the mighty Albion Rovers in the Scottish Cup, for one thing. And for another, it does not seem to have been a safe place to be. Unless you were a fox that is.

I am told that they were in a field of turnips with real expectations of putting up a pheasant or two and something like a guarantee of some lively partridge.

A shout got up. "Fox! Fox coming up the drill! Fox coming up the drill towards you Mossie! Fox coming right at you Moss!"

It's not like Mossie to get flustered but he made such a hash of shooting that fox as to make everyone else's day. "Where, where?" he cried anxiously, waving his gun at the skies where he might have seen the expected game birds but had no hope of seeing the fox.

It came right up the drill at him and was swerving to avoid bumping into him when the hero finally focussed. To cut a disgraceful story short, the big game hunter eventually got off both barrels but missed when it would have been much easier to hit the fox.

Everyone, including the fox, was delighted of course, and poor Moss had to suffer dog's derision for an hour or so.

But help was at hand.

As will happen from time

to time, someone got over excited when a covey of low partridges were put up and, unable to wait for the birds to clear the lines, he let go with both barrels. It was some shot. He had a left and a right and an 'out the back'. It is just bad luck that the Rooster presents such a big target, but he got a pellet in the cheek only an inch or so below the eye.

Now the reason I'm glad I wasn't at the shoot is because of what didn't happen next.

I always understood that if that happened, as it will if boys will play with dangerous toys, the sportsman in question was supposed to put his gun back in its case. In the embarrassing event of his failing to do so, the host should instruct him to retire from the field.

But all that happened in this case was that the level of hilarity fell a bit. Mossie was delighted, however. As he put it, "It took the pressure off me for missin that fox."

It would be a horrendous thing to have to do. I certainly wouldn't like to have to tell one of my guests to go home, but really, these parts of the country code are important.

That was borne in on me early. When I was about seven, the grieve here had one of the few dogs I have ever liked. It was a working collie which spent most of its life rather miserably, tied to a chain which limited its world to ten feet or so round the coal shed.

Poor Mirk might have spent many more miserable years had it been tied even more. For a man appeared in the close one day and told the grieve his dog

103

had been seen among his sheep. Old Jimmy Low simply went into the house, brought out his ancient single-shot twelve bore and shot Mirk dead. He never had another working dog unless you think terriers who chase rats are working.

I think maybe the injured Rooster agrees that sterner action might have been taken. It's not that he said so, I just think that on account of what he did when they were tallying up the bag at the end of the day.

That's when they lay all the poor unfortunates out on the grass. The pheasants and partridges in brace, a cock and hen lying sadly side by side, then all the pigeons, the hares and the rabbits in serried ranks. They left a big gap between the hares and rabbits of course, "That's the space for foxes," said the host amid ribald laughter.

"So that's forty-five kills atween ten guns, boys. Nae bad considerin some werena shootin that well." More leering in the direction of poor Moss.

But Mossie's not easy to beat. "Oh ay, and have you coontit the Rooster?" he said and looked deliberately back at the game.

And there was the Rooster, lying, as though at peace, between the pheasants and the partridges, a little blood still trickling from the wound on his cheek.

Oh no. I'm better out of the A team.

I'd like to be among the top boys when it comes to growing the crops though. There's real money in that. And things are looking quite promising there. Despite the winter frosts the November sown wheat has finally struggled into the light of day, not that there's much of that, in Aberdeenshire in January. Everything else is looking as well as can be expected and we'll have a good year if we get the spraying right and if there's some weather there to catch.

But there is a huge cloud hanging over Little Ardo. My forty-five cows that should calve in March have started already. I had two aborted this morning.

The vet's been and he's away with samples. The results will be the difference between disappointment and disaster.

Innovating farmer par excellence

A WALKING stick has just come into my possession. It is a good strong stick and with the arthritic lumps growing steadily on knees which once carried me to the world championship at caber tossing, there is definitely a job for it here.

And yet I am not sure that I should keep it.

The first owner was my grandfather, the late Dr Maitland Mackie. It was presented to him by the company when he resigned in 1969 from the board of the pig-processing firm, Lawsons of Dyce. Maitland Mackie was one of the founding investors when the company was set up in the 1930s, having put in the magnificent sum of £200. It is a cane stick with a horn tip and a suitably inscribed gold ring.

An Agriculture College governor, NFU president, and innovating farmer par excellence, old Dr Maitland Mackie (the current NFU vice-president's grandfather) was also a gentleman and universally admired, not least by those who worked for him.

By no means the least of those was James Low. They met first at Ellon Feeing Market in 1930. Maitland Mackie wanted Low, of whom he knew by his reputation, which was both hard and keen.

Now, Maitland Mackie normally got the men he wanted because, as well as providing above-average housing and the chance to work with good equipment, he always offered a couple of pounds above the going rate for the half year.

But one of the features of the feeing markets in those hard times was that they provided the men with a rare opportunity to speak to their masters on the basis of equality, however temporary. As Low himself told me, "Ye could say what ye liked to them until your bargain was struck, so we used to cheek them up."

And Low did not waste the opportunity to get a good hit or two in at one of the most famous farmers in the county.

Mackie had gone into seed potatoes in a big way and, in those days before conveyer

105

belts and bulk handling, that meant a lot of hard graft for the men in winter time.

"Na" said Low, 'I'm nae comin." "Why not?" said Maitland Mackie. "Ye hinna got a very good reputation." "And how's that?" "Well, your men gang about wi a bag on their back aa winter."

The farmer refused, with perfect humour, to rise to the bait. "You might think better of me if once you were home to North Ythsie," he said simply and with a little smile.

Maitland Mackie, who said many true words in his ninety years, never said truer words than those.

Low did fee as second horseman at North Ythsie. He stayed for two years, and at the early age of, twenty-nine, was put to Mackie's out-farm of Little Ardo as grieve. He had sole charge of 230 acres, feeding cattle, and more hens than seems reasonable.

And the story of how he reacted when the incubating house burned down, may give us some guidance as to why James Low thought so well of his employer. Huge numbers of hens were lost, and the shed demolished totally.

Low phoned Mackie, who said he would be over as soon as he could. Low spent a miserable day wondering if he should leave then, or wait and see if he might get away with a bawling out - and be able to stay until the end of his yearly contract.

Maitland Mackie didn't appear till the next day, but when he did come he was not alone. He had a builder with him. "Now grieve, we'd better not have a wooden shed this time. And are there any other improvements we could make?" The farmer didn't even seek to know how the fire had started, let alone start to apportion blame. He knew his man would have done his best, and that his best was very good indeed.

There is no doubt, it was partly because Low was there that Maitland Mackie decided to put his son-in-law, John R. Allan, into Little Ardo after he ceased to be Captain Allan at the end of the war. He was known to be a writer, but if he proved to be a middling farmer, Low would keep him right.

So he did. And from 1973 until he retired finally and left the place in 1976, James Low looked after me.

When Maitland Mackie died in 1974, his family decided it would be be appropriate, and appreciated, if his old grieve were to get his presentation walking stick. Indeed it was. I can remember the warmth with which the grieve told me of his gift of the old man's stick.

When the grieve in his turn died, his widow gave it to her son James Low jr, who is now retired himself and living in the village below Little Ardo.

And so it was that, last Sunday when I was feeding the cows, this man who was no longer young, and might have been his father with his rolling rural gait, appeared in the close and presented me with my grandfather's walking stick.

He feels that it is my family's, and should be at Little Ardo.

I'm not sure that he is right. It was given by the Lawson's of Dyce to my family in recognition of their debt to my grandfather. And my family gave it to James Low in recognition of his service to them. And I'm damned if I am going to give it back to the Lawsons.

And if it is to come back into my family, should it not go to the Maitland Mackie who is the old man's great-grandson?

Luckily, I now have the upper hand, and James Low jr feels the stick that marries our two families should be at Little Ardo where his father and mother spent all but the first few of their working years.

So I guess it should stay here. Then again, a year ago, I sold a corner of Little Ardo for a grandson of James Low to build a house on. Perhaps he should get it. At any rate it is a stick with a provenance.

107

Twenty-four per-cent of very little

I'VE JUST been reading that farm incomes are up by 24 percent. Sir Hector Monro is reported to have welcomed the figures as being "extremely good news". Perhaps I'm in a bad mood but, despite the fact that the news can hardly be anything but good (if it's true), the reading annoyed me.

Here's why. Firstly, the average is not what interests me, and my income is down. The pigs were down and would have been a disaster had I not had the unusual good sense not to buy any replacements for my last batch. The winter rape was a record, but all the other crops were down.

We did better with the calves this year though. We could hardly have failed as the proportion of half-Jerseys went down from seventy to twenty-five percent. All in all, I'm in profit, but a smaller profit than last year.

Secondly, these percentages need very careful handling. To let newspaper headline writers loose on them, is to ask to be misled. If your income is one pound one year and the next year it is still virtually nothing - say, a hundred pounds that is a percentage rise of ten thousand.

And that is exactly what is the matter with this rise in farm incomes of 24 percent. After thirty years of falling incomes it is 24 percent of very little.

And another statistical freak of percentages can be illustrated by a little story of Grumpy Allan, the farmer who was always complaining that he was hard done by. One year, Grumpy's profit went up from £5000 to £10,000 and the next year it fell back to £5000 again. Grumpy made a hellova fuss about that, but the clever people at the Ministry of Agriculture couldn't see what he was complaining about. His income might have fallen 50 percent this year but, after all, it had risen 100 percent last year.

Thirdly, we need a figure that has some absolute value if we are to get a useful idea of how we are really getting on. Something like "return on capital employed" would do.

And everyone knows the return on capital employed in agriculture is laughable.

Little Ardo is not worth less than £400,000. I haven't got much machinery but for ease of counting let's say that, with the cattle, it's a half million pound deal. I don't think I've ever made £25,000 off it which would be 5 percent , and I did once lose £17,000 or 3.4 percent. I'd settle for 1 percent, year on year.

Now, how much more informative it is to talk of this year's improvement as being, not 24 percent but an increase in the return on capital from 1 percent to 1.24 percent. If Agriculture Minister Monro talked about a rise in the profitability of Scottish farming of one quarter of a percent I'd be better pleased with him, and better prepared to listen.

Fourthly, almost exactly half of that supposed rise was nothing to do with farming - it was all to do with interest rates, which had been deliberately kept high throughout this Government's time in office. The only reason interest rates had slumped was that the speculators had forced the government to abandon its policy.

Then the English were up over 43 percent, and from a much higher base, despite the twin handicaps of being English and being less good at farming than we are.

And finally, I am close to despair at the comparison between the total profits of Scottish farms and the total subsidy bill for keeping us going. The government spent £282 million supporting us and yet we only made £228 million. It looks like all we farmers did by our efforts was to lose 15 percent of our hand-out.

If they'd given us the money, and we'd done nothing at all with our land, we'd have been much better off.

Can this really be?

Yes indeed it can.

The government makes us do all sorts of crazy things to qualify for the subsidies. It makes it worth our while sowing worthless crops of linseed, and uneconomic crops of oil-seed rape. Despite the fact that there is too much beef, they will only give us the beef cow subsidies if we keep cattle.

Now I know that the Government has many objectives in its policy, and that it may be subsidising the keeping of sheep because it likes to see sheep on the hills. So do I, but for goodness sake could they not make that explicit instead of giving everyone the impression that agricultural subsidies are there to support us poor farmers.

Were that the only case, they would surely give us the money and let us do what we liked with our land. If they did, most of us would find a profitable use for the land, and it is my guess that most of that would be farming.

I'm sorry I've been so serious. Maybe it's the fact that the Jag has had its first major breakdown.

One frosty morning, I noticed that each time I accelerated, the wheels seemed to spin.

That wouldn't have been too surprising as it was a very frosty morning. However, it soon became apparent that there was something seriously amiss. I was revving her up and going nowhere.

A new clutch for a Jag would be bad enough, but a new clutch for an automatic Jag might be prohibitive. I eventually discovered an oil leak, borrowed a gallon of transmission fluid, and limped home.

That was a month ago, and the Jaggy has been in a most expensive dry dock ever since.

Mind you, it's not all my loss. What a difference there is in my fuel bill now that I am back to the two old Cavaliers. The man from the filling station has been pleading with the mechanic to get her back on the road quickly, and Potions tells me there are rumours of short-time working at Grangemouth.

110

February 14, 1994

Amateur cowboys to blame

THINGS ARE not as bad as I thought they were on the land of my fathers. Mind you, they did look bad for a while.

You will recall that bleak day three weeks ago when I discovered not one, but two of my March/April calvers had aborted. It was certainly unexpected. In my time we've never had brucellosis. We'd had our herd test in November and a clean bill of health.

Since then not a single beast had been bought in. The bull hadn't even been away for his holidays.

But still contagious abortion did look likely, and the vet insisted on isolation of the two abortees. It began to look like a brucella convention the next day when, among the uncalved cows, I again saw a cow looking awkward. She was standing by herself and shifting from foot to foot with her back up. When I eventually got round behind her, sure enough, there was a tale-telling bit of membrane hanging out of her.

I phoned the vet. He would come and take more samples, though by this time we were all convinced we had had a breakdown.

It was Potions the chemist who broke the news to the boys down at the Salmon on Sunday. I just didn't feel like going. They say that a trouble shared is a trouble halved, but not with that lot. If you share a trouble with them it is multiplied by the number there, and, if the trouble is great enough, it is soon multiplied by everyone who is in touch with a phone.

I am told that the news of my breakdown caused a moment of shocked silence which lasted for over a second. "Mind you," said the Red Rooster at last. "you could see it comin."

"Oh aye," said Mossie, who still hasn't forgiven me for feigning injury to get out of going on his £120 a day pheasant shoot, "he has been actin a bitty queer."

"Peer loon," said Hamish. "I suppose we'll need an election for a new chairman of the discussion group. Mind you, the grun's warmin up. We'll

111

soon get the first of the manure on."

And so I might have passed into history.

But things started to get better on Monday.

It was dinner-time when the Wasting Asset burst excitedly in. How he had managed to get up and do all that reading already I did not try to guess, but he had read that the compensation for cows slaughtered in a brucellosis breakdown were to be compensated at three-quarters of £1375, or the market price, whatever was the smaller. He thought we'd easy be able to talk the market price up to that. So we could get £1000 a piece for the cows. If they all had brucellosis we'd get £50,000, sell the quota, and do like Mossie says and just grow crops and have an easy life.

Then came the call from the vet. He'd noticed two of the cows seemed to have the same number.

Well, if I'd given the same number to two beasts it wouldn't be the first time, but it was much worse than that and, as it turned out, much better.

I am certainly not going to put my hand up for this blunder, so I can only blame my two amateur assistants. You see, when I was isolating the two aborted cows I had assistance from Potions the chemist and the Wasting Asset (my younger son who helps between parties as part-payment of the rent of his cottage). Somehow this ropey posse of cowboys had isolated the wrong beast.

112

So, when the next day I saw this obviously aborted cow, it was one of those I'd seen already.

My brucellosis epidemic was down to two.

And then I got the results of the tests. Neither was positive. No brucella, no compensation, and no quiet life was in prospect after all.

I am glad, of course. When my father sold his dairy herd, back in the 60s, it was bought by a man who had had severe problems with brucellosis. It is said that he replaced too soon and that most of our fine herd of black and whites had to be slaughtered. I'm glad that's not going to happen this time.

That herd, which was destroyed before the days of Holstein skin-and-bone cattle, was one of the five founded by my grandfather, and in its heyday had always been both the smallest and produced the best figures. That was a source of great pride to me throughout my childhood.

I cannot claim much for my current herd of hill cows. Thank goodness there are no published figures of the kind that allowed my father to make the most detailed comparisons with every other dairy herd in the county.

They are little more than accidents of history. There are still a few remnants of my disastrous, if plucky, attempt to run a herd of transplanted Jersey hill cows, but most are Black Herefords who were unlucky enough to find themselves in a batch of 30 heifers on the market at the right time at £65 a head.

But there is one part of the herd which is interesting and could yet be a source of pride - or even profit.

In 1970 I founded one of the original herds of Simmental cattle in Britain. They have long since been sold - though I did hang on to two which, for different reasons, could not be presented for a society sale. I've kept on registering one now and again, and I now have some ten pure Simmentals. The Ardo herd may be a pale shadow of that which produced Perth and Highland Show champions in the seventies but it would have been sad to see them go finally, for all the attractions of the quiet life.

February 21, 1994

Weather girls are the limit

THE WEATHER forecasters really are the limit. I may be wrong, but I see their job as being to tell us what they can about the prospects for the country's weather - aye, all of the countries' weather. But they clearly see it differently.

There we were on Monday last, catching the news before going out to get on with the farm work, and this pretty girl told us in all seriousness that the big question was: "Will we be able to get home from work?"

Well, that might have been the big question for her, but it was going to be a hellova day to stop me getting from the tractor shed back to the kitchen.

Of course, the pretty girl thinks that London weather is what counts, and that she is there to inform commuters about what to expect. They'd had a bit of snow and, as usual, their drivers were causing chaos. But whatever the big question was in Methlick it certainly wasn't whether the farmers would be able to get back to the house after the morning's work.

And then there was another pretty girl. She's based in Glasgow, so no doubt she thinks the weather forecast is about what to expect in Glasgow. So it is, but that is not all it's about. "Now let's see if the weather can possibly get any worse," said the pretty girl.

Any worse? It could hardly have got any better here in Aberdeenshire. It was a fine clear day with a firm frost on the ground. The farmers were busy. Some were on the land, taking the chance when it was hard and dry to get off the stones that had been missed at the back end. Many were putting out muck and Mossie, just to be in front as usual, was putting the sulphur on the winter rape.

There may have been snow where the weather girls live, but we didn't have one flake. Indeed, we had had a fine drying wind for three days and, combined with the occasional touch of frost, it had dried up all the straw that had to be left in what would have been the autumn. Those with barley straw were

114

able to get it burned to clear the land for the spring work, and those with wheat straw were able to solve the only real problem of this winter, the shortage of bedding, by baling it.

On this terrible day, when all the pretty weather forecasters in their offices wondered if the weather could get worse and if we'd win home, we baled thirty-four acres of wheat straw in absolutely perfect order.

I don't mind them being rotten at forecasting, but I hate the arrogance of their assumption that their weather is more important than mine.

The baling of the wheat straw is not all good news. You will recall my strategy for getting my cows through the winter? I would sow more

cereals, make less silage and sell straw to buy silage.

This has looked like a smart move with straw making as much as £10 a bale ex the farm, and silage to be had for as little as £7 delivered.

Indeed, I've had about £1000 worth of that silage so far. That side of the deal has worked well.

Unfortunately, I haven't been getting on with the sale of straw. I did offer some to one of the volume buyers a couple of weeks back, but he was down to a fiver - and he'd stopped buying meantime.

After this superb dry spell I have loads of straw, I am keen to sell, and a fiver looks fine. But so has everyone else - and a fiver looks high.

Once more, a best laid

scheme of this man is up the spout.

I suppose we could use the straw to cash in on the recovery of the pig market. They've been losing a tenner a pig for months now, and must be due for a rise. Indeed, it has started already with the market price up to 88 pence as I write. With the break-even point at about £1, it is still not a bad industry to be out of, but the theory is that if you get in and stay in the price is bound to go above £1 again someday.

So should I try some weaners?

Well, I've made enquiries and it seems that those who have made all those losses when the price has been down are reluctant to sell now that it's on the rise.

I wish them luck. I'm not going to chase the market.

Isn't it amazing how the pheasants know when it's into February and the shooting season is over? It's not just that they know when you have a gun with you. See ten pheasants in a field. Run home for the gun. Now there are no pheasants in the field.

It is more than that. Whereas you might see five pheasants in the field on the 31st of January, there will be at least ten in the fields on the 1st of February. Where do they go? And where do they come from?

When we were taking in the bales this week there were twenty-one in one of our fields; one of those same fields that yielded one kill per gun at Potion's last shoot of the season.

The pheasants are celebrating - and so is Nicol from Keith's partner. All the shooting that Nicol and Mossie had been doing had left very little time for business. And with the serious public relations dos like the Motor Trader's Dinner on top of the Burns circuit, there had been a few dizzy mornings when he had chosen to "work from home."

Anyway, when Nicol from Keith struggled in one morning, a couple of weeks back, he met his partner in the foyer. He was greeted with, "Can I help you sir. Would you like to see some brochures - ?"

116

February 28, 1994

King of show for £16,000

WE'RE USED to seeing thirty or forty acres of cars in a field at major agricultural events. But those are mostly in the summer. It was odd seeing them all lined up in the snow on Tuesday, and the five thousand slithering and sliding their ways into Thainstone Agricultural Centre at Inverurie for the Spring Show.

I must admit that I sometimes dodge the column when it comes to the Spring Show. It is a bit of an assault course. But there was no way I could miss this year's. You see my new tractor was to be on display.

There are farms and farmers for whom the imminent arrival of a new tractor is a matter of no importance. But this will be the first new tractor home to Little Ardo for 34 years. At a stroke, I will be trebling the book value of my machinery.

The last shiny tractor was the Fordson Major my father bought in 1960. I was away being a student and had far more important things to worry about, so I wasn't much touched by its arrival. But my mother used to tell me often about the anguish that went into that purchase.

She was the daughter of a farmer who was used to borrowing money and getting on. But John Allan was brought up by his grandparents, and his autobiography, Farmer's Boy starts: "I was born on the afternoon of the day when my grandfather signed his third trust deed on behoof of his creditors." His grandparents left him educated and rich in memories, but penniless - and he hated to be in debt.

That is a bad phobia to have if you're a farmer, and he had an overdraft of two or three thousand pounds, which troubled him until he retired and passed it on to me.

Anyway, there had been a desperate need for a new tractor as machinery grew heavier. They could see that the job would be done twice as fast if they got two-furrow ploughs. But a new tractor meant increasing the overdraft, and my father spent sleepless nights.

It was my mother, financial genius though she was not, who solved the problem. If he took it on HP, he would never notice the payments. It worked. For some reason, being in hawk to the finance companies at a higher rate of interest, wasn't as bad as owing to the banks. The great machine, with its live-drive clutch, its smart plywood cab, and with glass in the front and sides, came home to Little Ardo.

It cost £800, and its successor is priced at £16,000 for what is the successor to the Massey-Ferguson 590 but is called an URSUS, and is made with sweated labour in the Czech Republic.

Remembering my father, I told the salesman to forget the finance companies. I would pay cash.

But that was last May, when I was looking eagerly forward to a bounteous harvest.

Now that the harvest is in, I've changed my mind. History has repeated itself, and the new tractor is on tick.

In breathless excitement I slithered round to the Port Services' stand, and there she was, looking a picture. And, no expense spared, there was a pencil written notice on what had been the inside of a cornflakes packet, proclaiming "Sold to Charlie Allan." All my life I've admired signs like that but I never saw one I liked better. I jumped aboard, started her up and was king of the show.

But not for long. The boys have ways of bringing you

down to earth. Those who are used to spending £30,000 or £40,000 on a new tractor aren't going even to pretend to be impressed by a tractor costing £16,000 even if it has got twin rams, whatever that is.

After a quick sprint round the show, they had congregated in the Bennachie Bar.

"Tak a good look at her, Charlie. She'll never even look as good as that again," Hamish shouted, no more cruelly than expected.

"I ken about Back to Basics, but there was nae need for Charlie to go that far," said Crookie, who would get eight of my tractors if he could get back the price he paid for his latest combine.

I was thankful that my tractor was such a small event for they soon passed on to bigger fish. The rise in the price of land may give Hamish a chance to be rid of Slains castle and her seven hundred acres beside (and sometimes in) the North Sea. Of course he would no longer be a baron, but the boys feel that he should sell.

Certainly Hamish wasn't looking much like a baron at the Spring Show. He appeared to have slept in his shirt which prompted Mossie to make the smart-assed remark that he wasn't in need of more land so much as a new iron.

No slouch with the cruelty when the focus moves to someone else, I offered, "Your best hope there Hamish, is a deep-water port."

"God, aye," says Mossie, "You'd be able to get a boat to rin alongside the combine and load on the move."

Of course it wasn't all work at the Spring Show. We did see some sights.

Like the six months old Limousin cross calf, which was presented for sale without signs of having won any prizes, and which was run up to £1500 before being withdrawn. We did see two people bidding, so it looked genuine. That was five pounds a kilo so it was already, at six months old, in the position of having to win Smithfield to justify its price.

And on the Osmonds' stand they tried to sell me a feed additive that did everything desirable to growing cattle without drugs, antibiotics, smell, or worry. The only snag with Muscle Master, according to Charles Wilson is, "If you're feeding thistles and chappit neeps it is nae use ava."

As I am trying to do just that, without the neeps, it clearly has no place at Little Ardo.

119

Shocked by the cruelty implied

IT HAS been a sober week. The boys are really depressed.

It's not the weather that has depressed them, though goodness knows that has been bad enough. We had an inch and a half of rain on the first day of March. That melted most of the snow into floods. We had the first storm in October in what should have been our Indian summer. We have had a storm in every month since, and who's to say there won't be another storm in April to give us a seven-month winter.

But it wasn't that which upset the discussion group.

It wasn't even the threats of which we seem to hear more each day; threats of cuts in the subsidies. According to Mossie, my honorary crops adviser, the likely cuts in oil-seed rape acreage payments have brought feeding spring barley back into consideration on the second class land of Aberdeenshire. That seems like a giant step backward to me.

Don't get me wrong. It will be a step towards sanity for the industry, but, in cash flow terms, I don't like the look of it. Two hundred pounds an acre to grow an uneconomic crop always looked like a bargain to me.

No, no. It was that item on the tele that took the swagger out of our steps. In case you missed it, what was shown was a home-made video, on the basis of which the Scottish Society for the Prevention of Cruelty to Animals raided a pig farm. It appeared to show healthy pigs sharing a pen with the dying, the dead, and the dead long since. One slurry table was above slat level and, among other horrors, a tethered sow appeared to be having her litter on slats.

Of course we didn't all see it, but Big Hamish is quick with the record button, and he'd managed to get a copy. Several of us went to see it together.

It is hard to describe the reaction, but I can say with confidence that I never saw us so at a loss for words. For once there were no jokes. There was a sort of mildly hysterical silence.

I may have got it wrong, but I think the boys were shocked in three ways. First, they were shocked by the cruelty implied. They were also shocked by what this sort of publicity does to the image of our industry (not that there has ever been anything like it before). But most of all we were hurt that the impression should be put about that the sort of stockmanship implied is in any way normal, or acceptable, in the industry.

It isn't.

Life must go on, thankfully, and we tried to put our humiliations aside by surging on with the duties of the day. Like driving down to the village for the papers in the brand new tractor.

I wonder if my father drove his shiny new Fordson Major down for the papers when she came home in 1960. If he did, it would have been in large part in the hope of catching James Presly whose farm of Wardford glowers north across the Ythan valley at us. But James would have heard about the new tractor and would have avoided the village for a day or two. Mr Presly is still there but I knew I had no hope that he would be at the shop as he would undoubtedly have heard of my purchase.

I must say I was a bit disappointed with my run, because I was a few minutes late, and several of the regulars had gone by the time I purred up to the shop, cosy in my heated and wind-proof cab, tuned in to Classic FM - which happened to have a burst of Schubert on.

It is interesting to observe folk on such occasions in an agricultural village.

Some will patronise you with, "Things must be a bit better at the head of the hill, are they?" and "It's nae really that bad, for a tractor from the Third World."

A few will be genuinely pleased for you, and interested to see if a tractor made in the Czech Republic can go, and whether it has lights, and a dashboard. They will be impressed that it has a rev-counter, and astonished that it has twin rams as standard.

And there are those who pretend not to have seen you. They turn their backs, or gaze in fascination at the small advertisements in the shop window. Those I like best, because they are truly impressed.

And I soon had a chance to impress them again. The Breadwinner, who was at home instead of away winning bread, mentioned at coffee time that she was short of milk. Having no more than fifty-one cows I just had to go down to the shop.

I took the tractor as it was handy.

I also had two trips to the smiddy and one to the garage for a penny washer.

Which reminds me, we have a new member of our discussion group. He's our first White Settler and as such completes the set. He has bought a little croft on the cold side of Little Ardo. From there he makes enough money in the oil business to keep several horses, dogs and cows.

For all his expensive hobbies this man knows the value of a penny. He appeared at the hardware division of the local garage one day last week in search of a penny washer.

"Certainly sir. That'll be sixteen pence."

"What! You're not going to charge me sixteen pence for a penny washer? Now I know all about inflation. I'd be cheaper going home and drilling a hole in a ten pence piece." And so he did.

Quite right too. There are only two disadvantages to his course of action. First and least, it is illegal to deface the coinage. And second, he is now stuck with the nickname of "Penny Washers".

Discussion group being undermined

MY GRANNY, with whom, during the war, I spent some of my most formative time, was a Christian who believed that the Lord really meant it about keeping the Sabbath holy. I remember her giving her husband a hard time when, at the tail end of a very difficult harvest, he couldn't resist taking advantage of a wonderful drying day to get some stooks home.

She also gave him such a hard time of it over the demon drink, that by the time I knew my grandfather he was all but teetotal (an Australian sherry at the New Year).

That is why I shudder to think what she would have made of the on-goings at the Salmon Inn on Sunday. Truthfully, I didn't think much of them myself, as they cut right across our discussion group. For several years now, at eight o'clock on a Sunday, we have met to discuss strategy for the coming week, to exchange news of bargains to be had, to criticise our political leaders, and to do our bit for the malting barley trade.

But now we are quite undermined.

At four o'clock on Sundays there is a great party gets up at the Salmon. There are a lot of shooters with wives who don't like cleaning game, and children who only know how to eat fish fingers. They bring along their bags and bung them on the barbecue that Mossie made out of the old muckspreader. On Sunday there was even a roe deer, and the dredgings from someone's deepfreeze.

Mine hostess puts up tatties and salads, as well as all the drink that money can buy. A jolly time is had by all.

"So what's the problem?" I hear you ask. "Can't you just have your discussion group earlier?"

Well, yes, but you see the wives come too. Indeed, I see the whole deal as an infernal scheme to insinuate that woman's lib thing into this previously unsullied corner of civilisation. And we can't really argue. We can make a case for having family supper, and then nipping out for a couple of hours with the boys. But they're hardly going to let us out to an afternoon barbecue without them.

And on Sunday it was worse than that. There were at least fifty children playing hide-and-seek among the boozers, and asking where the fish fingers were at buffet time.

Crookie was there with his new baby. Potions was there with his two, and Mossie's three were there. The Recovery Stock was there with his two, and the eldest of my Investments was there with her two. Now I ask you, how can a man participate properly in a discussion group when he has four grandchildren pulling at him?

Mind you, I did get a while at the bar with Mossie, though I really wished I hadn't. He's got me quite cross. We were discussing the manure requirements for the grazing season, and he said quite casually: "Of course you're sookin the farm, so you'll just be needin nitrogen."

What a damned cheek. How very unkind - and how untrue.

Mind you, I could give the farm a good sook before I retire in five years time.

I could give up altogether on the lime, the potash, the phosphates, the trace elements and seaweed. That would do most of its damage after I've retired. All I need do for the remaining five years is to haud on the nitrogen.

I can sell all my heifers and let the age of the herd rise. That'll mean I can keep the old bull, instead of renewing him when he comes over his own stock.

During the years of the sook I need put up no new fences, and do only the merest repair jobs around the steading. Every spare penny can be salted away out of the business into a nice bungalow.

The bungalow, or death house, to which the Farmer will retire should be on the best site on the farm. That means the best view, protection from the weather, and it should be far enough from the steading to make it difficult to help when there are breakouts, but near enough for frequent visits to criticise, and if possible to deride, the work of the next generation.

And that's where five years of sooking a place before he leaves can offer another bonus to the Farmer.

It is his most earnest wish to be able to come back and see that the farm is missing him. He craves the assurance that the next generation is not as good a farmer as he was. Now, a well organised sook can make sure of that.

If the land is properly sooked it will take the young a few years to rebuild its fertility. If there is five years' repair work to be done to the steadings and the fences, it won't look so well. And if it is seven years since a new bull was bought, the calves may not look so well and their old ladies will have bad feet.

As the next generation is likely to be short of capital, it may take them some years to repair the effects of a well-organised sook. The better the sook the longer the retired farmer will be able to come back and shake his head at the efforts of the young, and say: "It was never like that in my day."

Yes, I will have to give sooking the land serious consideration. I reckon, properly handled, it could add twenty thousand to my retirement fund.

If I don't do it, it will be for fear of my ancestors. Certainly my father would be shocked to think of me sooking the land. My grandfather would disown me, so shocked would he be.

But he wouldn't be half as shocked as his wife would be if she could see what they've done to the Sabbath at the Salmon Inn.

March 21, 1994

Mossie even paid me a compliment

THE SUN is shining, the manure is on, but there is very little sign of growth. The only thing that has moved at all is the winter rape, which has turned deepest green, and the leaves which were tired and frost-bitten have perked up and are ready to burgeon.

All we need now is heat - and lots of it.

If you let the number of fine sunny days be your guide, you'd really be looking hard for Spring. But for some reason the ground is taking longer than usual to warm up. The old men, who must know about such things for they talk of little else, say it is because of the winter being the wettest since the war.

There are harbingers of Spring though. The rabbits have become active in the garden, the first crop of the pigeons which nest in the piggery have fledged and been shot, and the first of the backwoodsmen who appear about this time have started to look for a few grazers.

I don't know if it is the thought of Spring and the promise of another growing season, but Mossie is in extraordinary good humour. He even paid me a compliment this week.

He came round on Tuesday, and we walked all the crops in glorious sunshine. Not that that made a lot of difference to us really, as Mossie's idea of a farm walk is to drive his fancy Land-Rover all over my delicate crops.

"Aye," he kept saying, "this is the way forward," as I jumped out to open yet another gate. "Plough and plant with the one-pass combination drill, and then do exactly as I tell ye for once as regards the manure and the sprays, and you'll get 100 percent - and that's the first time there's been 100 percent at this place."

I thought the last a gratuitous swipe, but I could see that this was a compliment coming from Mossie. My natural curiosity, and the desire to give him the chance to be even nicer about my crops, made me ask what exactly he meant by 100 percent.

Was 100 percent the best that crops could look?

"Dinna be daft, Charlie. 100 percent for you means 100 percent better than usual. In fact I'd go as far as to say that you're 200 percent this year - and, afore ye ask, that means 'as good as onybody roon aboot except Moss-side', of course."

Well, of course!

He showed me the light leaf spot just beginning to get going on the rape, and the rynchosporium on the winter barley. But he pronounced the rape "a show", the barley "an absolute show" and wheat "a million percent better than last year, when you used that home saved dirt instead of English seed".

I can't say I understand the great man's mathematics, but he's right. The wheat is even further behind than last year, but there are many more plants to fill the eye when the growth does start. As soon as the ground is dry enough, I'll be on with the roller to get it to tiller.

And I'll be spraying on the cycocel with my smart new tractor.

What a difference that makes. When I sprayed the rape last week, I realised again just how stupid I'd been to spray for so long with the old 590. For the first time for a long time, I finished the job without a sore head and it is easy to see why.

There was a gentle breeze from the west and as I sprayed from west to east, the tractor was quite enveloped in a cloud of environmenticide. That didn't bother me in my new

air-conditioned cab with windows and doors. But in the old 590 my eyes and throat would have been burning by the time I reached the endrigg.

Never again.

Of course, Mossie wasn't pleased with all my farming. He refuses even to look at my cattle. What do ye want wi them? You're just the working fool. All work and nae profit."

Well now, he does have a habit of being right and, when they have broken out again to trample the Breadwinner's lawn, or when I hear the roaring that could be a calving in the night, I do sometimes think of giving in. But then again, this is a stock farm. It is just because of Euro-nonsense that we are growing all these cereals and rape.

And just wait till he sees the cheque I'll get in April for my yearlings. The worst of them might still be no more than five hundredweight, but the best could be over nine. I have 22 heifers and 20 stotties to sell, so the banker had better brace himself to receive a cheque for £20,000.

Then, who'll be the "workin fool"?

Mind you, we meat producers are under pressure. A chat with an old friend who farms in Wiltshire added to my alarm on that score. He had been appalled at the scale of the problem facing us, suggested by the behaviour of the parent of three of the children he had invited to his son's seventh birthday party.

Yes, it would be fine for the children to come to the party, but, because they were vegans, a parent would have to come and check out the food.

"The children are free to choose what they like. We just think they should know what's in everything, so they can make an unbiassed choice."

So the father took the three guests round my friend's table and explained "There's baa baa in that," pointing to the mutton pies. "And that's oink oink...euch!" My friend hoped that the spinach quiche would pass muster, but no. "There's cluck cluck in that." Surely an apple tart would be alright? "Is that your own pastry make, without suet? Well children, you can eat that if you want to, but remember there is moo in it."

He might as well have said "poo" for all the freedom of choice that was.

How the coos ate Hamish's wet silage

I HAVE acquired a renewed respect for Big Hamish. Respect will always be due to a member of the Thousand Acre club, who is a baron of a historic ruin, who can reverse a tractor and cart down a narrow pass at thirty miles an hour, and who can wrestle the best two men in most companies. But my awe has reached new heights on account of how he handled me over the rotten silage.

I ended up a couple of hundred bales short this year and would sell my abundant straw to buy silage for my fifty-one cows and followers. Hamish could supply as many as I liked and would even deliver them. He started at £7 a bale and he's still only up to £8; and that's not dear considering it costs me a fiver just to cut, wrap and store the stuff we make here.

The snag was, the silage was of poor quality. There were only four days of sunshine from May through August, so it was no wonder the stuff was wet. But it was more than that. Too many bales were moulded and some were rotten. Sometimes the slatted shed was so full of steam after shaking out a bale, that I couldn't see the far wall.

Now, you will be familiar with the wimpish behaviour in restaurants whereby everyone chews away, complaining to one another about the dreadful food. It is cold. The meat is tough. The vegetables must have been leftovers from lunch. There's a greenfly in the lettuce, the potatoes too salty and the cream on the trifle is sour.

Then the waiter comes along and asks, "Everything alright for you, sir?"

"Yes lovely thanks - just beautiful," you hear yourself say. You are un-nourished and now humiliated. You even leave a tip rather than admit you had a lousy meal.

Well, I was a bit like that with Hamish's silage. I told everybody what dreadful stuff it was. And when the big man didn't turn up for the discussion group, I gave them all a good laugh and had them all shaking their heads about the terrible silage that Hamish was selling.

But when he came to collect his money on Wednesday it was, "Certainly Hamish. 100 bales at £7 a bale, that's £700 I'll be due you." I had meant to ask to be let off the half dozen or so that were really bad but. - you know how it is when the head waiter comes round and asks if your burnt steak was to your liking (which is rare).

But Hamish wasn't content with his money. He had a point to make. "Aye, but I hear you had the odd bad bale among them. I canna charge you for them. I've got my reputation to think about."

It was as though the head-waiter had said, "Come off it, sir. I know your steak had a big lump of gristle in it. Let me take six pounds off the bill."

"Oh well," says I, "That's very good of you Hamish. You give such a good service, delivering them at short notice and so on but, if you insist, there were maybe half a dozen that were pretty bad."

"I won't charge you for any that are nae good enough," says Hamish, "c'mon and we'll go an have a look at them."

And there he had me. I had only been feeding one bale a

130

day to my forty dry cows and, while they had plenty straw and promax as well as a few pounds of cake a day, they were not going to leave any silage lying about, just because it was wet and mouldy. "Oh no, you canna see it Hamish. The coos have eaten it."

"Now, Charlie, you canna expect me to give ye silage for neathing, when the cows have eaten it. You say it wasna good, but it's nae you that has to eat it."

That'll teach me to complain about Hamish behind his back - and I'm certainly not going to do it to his face.

Good silage or not, the calving season is in full swing. I'm a bit later than the others in the discussion group and I've a high standard to live up to.

Young Ochyoch, who didn't realise how lucky he was only to have cereals, went and bought himself twenty in-calf heifers. He paid a king's ransom for them so he has no hope of profit, but he seems to be making a good job. He and the wife (a daughter of the great heavyweight athlete Jay Scott of Inchmurrin and a great asset on the end of a calving rope), were out in the small hours of the morning calving their last one on Friday. That gave them a full house.

And the young laird, who had a horrendous time last year with a virus, had got 36 out of 35 when I got my first one. It was a heifer and was followed by a bull.

But things really started popping at two o'clock on Sunday morning. We had been down in the fat lands of the Mearns enjoying the hospitality of James Mackie, who has the good fortune to farm Bent, the best place in the Howe of the Mearns. James is said to have been asked at a farmers' Matter of Opinion, which farm in all the world would he like to farm if he couldn't have Bent. His reply was that he would like to have Burnton, the farm of James Anderson the Charolais breeder, as his second choice because, being just across the Howe from Bent, he would be able to look out every day and see the best farm in the Mearns.

Anyway, when we arrived home from what was a jolly occasion, I just popped my head into the shed in case there was anything calving.

What I found was a pure Simmental cow with a calf which looked as though it could live, and another which was flat out, but not yet dead. And there was a Black Hereford cow with a cold head and one leg sticking out. I'll tell you next week how I got on.

131

Off with the kilt - into a boilersuit

THE CALVING season being upon us, I would look round the cows when we got home at two o'clock. "Not in your best clothes you're not," said the Breadwinner. "I've had enough of that."

She was referring to the time twenty years ago when I came home from a Highland ball and would take a quick look at a pure Chianina heifer which was coming on for the calving. I had sold her sister to an American for "an undisclosed FIVE figure sum", so I was keen to get a live calf from this one. I wouldn't need to change, as I would be able to see how she was doing from the clean and dry floor at the end of the byre.

What greeted me when I put on the byre light was not good. About five thousand pounds worth of my calf was hanging out of the heifer and the other five thousand pounds worth would make all the difference. It was stuck at the heart, which means you have a couple of minutes to get it out. What could I do? Kilt and

all I flew into action. For once, everything was to hand and I got the American calf-puller on, and after an anxious few minutes had a live calf. It was a heifer, too, and that was what the market wanted.

I hadn't noticed that the pen could have been doing with more straw - a lot more straw. But the Breadwinner did. When I came in all smiles about my new calf, she threw a fit at the state of the Prince Charlie jacket, the kilt and the brogues. If you haven't done it, you'll have no idea how long it takes to get all the sharn out of those holes in the brogues and mine were ghillies.

She made me promise never to go near the cattle again without my working clothes, and I have not often.

So, it was on with the boilersuit when we got home last Sunday morning. And much need.

The first thing I saw when I turned on the light was a pure Simmental cow surveying what she had done. There was a bull calf sitting up, but looking in

132

poor shape and a heifer which turned out not to be dead - though she was cold, breathing very shallowly, and flat out.

Then there was a Hereford-Friesian cow with a head sticking out, and only one leg. The head was cold. I tried my finger in its mouth but got no response. It would be a job to get a one-legged dead calf out, but I was reluctant to add the expense of calling the vet out.

My father, had he come across such a scene, would have called the grieve and the cattleman. His contribution would have been to offer them a dram when they had finished. In the meantime, he'd have passed the time wetting the baby's head in anticipation.

How the lot of the farmer has changed. I had no staff on whom to call, I didn't know where to start, and I had already done more head-wetting than was seemly.

Maybe I should have got some colostrum into the twin bull, which had some potential for life but, instead, I decided to go for the one-legged calf. I supposed I might yet get a live calf, but also the cow deserved help.

I tried hard to get the missing leg forward but it was totally jammed. I put on the ropes and tried to muscle it out. And then I decided to give it a try with the calf-puller. Nothing was where it should have been. Eventually, I improvised for what I couldn't find, and set about pulling.

133

With an American calf-puller you have almost unlimited power, so you have to be careful. I put on as much pressure as I dared, but she was stuck. The only hope seemed to be to do a Caesarean and pull the head back in. I would call the vet. Why should he sleep on, when it was four o'clock in a fine morning?

Then, as luck will, mine turned.

I was trying to release the pressure on the calf when, quite suddenly, it started to move and then came away relatively easily.

That was good, but better was to follow. To my absolute astonishment the calf started to breath, the cow jumped up and started licking it. In minutes 'nightmare scenario' had become 'idyllic scene'.

But that was only half the problem. The twins were not doing well. There was no hope of the bull getting up to suck in the six hours we allow them, so I'd have to feed it. There was no hope for the heifer at all but, as a likely freemartin, that could be no loss, especially as the bull would be the better of the extra milk.

It was six o'clock when I arrived back from one of the local dairies, and got some colostrum into the bull calf. He perked up immediately. Things were sorting themselves out.

The heifer was still cold, but she was still breathing, so I thought there was no harm in giving her some colostrum too. She could never have drunk it, but I have one of those bags for putting it right into the stomach.

Well, it was like magic. In a minute she was shaking her head - and in five she was sitting up.

In the meantime, two other ladies had done the business without bother.

The calving is going well. The twins are still small. Their mother hasn't enough milk, but they are alive. I now have sixteen calves from fourteen cows, and the calving is off to a flier.

It's not all beer and skittles

THE CALVING goes well. We have twenty-seven calves from twenty-five cows and no deaths so far. I only need another 14.6 live calves to be up to quota. I know that it is common as muck for some farmers to have trouble-free calvings, but it isn't at Little Ardo.

My father used to have a dairy here, and he always had trouble. With the benefit of hindsight, and now that I am the veteran of hundreds of disastrous calvings, I think one of his troubles was he, or rather his staff, were too anxious to intervene.

Old Jimmy Low, the grieve who terrorised the place for more than forty years, used to say: "When the water's aff it's time they were oot o' that." We consider that four hours later is the time to go for the American calf-puller.

At any rate, in the forties and fifties, I can remember some awful calvings of Freisian heifers. They were 'steamed up' so that they'd be ready to flood the dairy with wealth-giving milk, but it made them too fat for the calving. I think it was after a run of disasters that my father and the grieve met in the close one day and decided to retire.

My father would let out the grass, and old Jimmy would stay on to mend the fences and make sure that as much as possible of the old steading would be saved.

When I brought cows back to Little Ardo in 1970 it was continental heifers, imported at huge expense, with a view to exporting their calves at even huger prices.

We started with Charolais heifers. They would just be the worst calvers in the world and, as we wanted pure calves, we couldn't give them an easy start with the black bull. Then we had Simmentals, Gelbvieh, Romagnola, Marchigiana, Chianina and Blondes d'Aquitaine. They were better calvers, but they were all heifers and, greedy to have more than one calf a year off our continental cows, we transplanted them and had more heifers to calve.

Then, as you know, in the

nineties I tried my Jersey hill-cow herd. I don't really know what went wrong there but again my calvings were far from trouble-free. Indeed, my calving percentages with the Jerseys might have made the Guinness Book of Records for all the wrong reasons.

So this year is really the first of my having a straightforward beef-cow herd with no heifers in it. And I like the idea that you give a small help only when something is amiss. So far, all that has gone wrong is that two of them came out with one leg back. However they came away reasonably easily.

Potions the chemist even calved one this year. I had to go to the mart and left him proudly in charge.

No sooner had I left than things started to happen. Two feet appeared at the back of one cow, and soon there was a nose. Potions decided to have one pull at the feet before panicking altogether, and going to see if he could find and operate the American calf-puller.

The cow was down and pushing hard, and he got a good grip of one foot in each hand and, bracing his feet against the cows hurdies gave an almighty heave. The calf came away so easily that he landed flat on his back with the calf on top of him. It is a fine bull calf, and he's convinced that the cow would never have managed had he not been on hand.

Even the twins are still with us, though they have a shortage of milk - and one of the heifers is giving cause for concern. I

am giving her a supplementary feed twice a day, and expect her to survive.

But poor old Penny Washers, the white settler, isn't doing so well. His calving is over, and he's achieved a calving percentage of sixty-six. Worse than that, the rate of attrition among his cows is also thirty-three percent.

Of course, that's not hard to do if you've only got three heifers calving. One had a dead calf delivered by caesar, and then the cow died.

He's doing better with the sheep though. He bought three hundred Shetland cross and Jacob ewes and has been getting lots of lambs. He's been doing a roaring trade in the Jacobs, selling ewes with twins for up to a hundred pounds to the settler community.

But even there he's discovering that farming isn't all beer and skittles. He arrived at the discussion group this week with a cardboard box, and placed this by the fire in the snug at the Salmon Inn.

This turned out to be a very sick, sick lamb - alive but cold and stretching its head backward in that pitiful gesture which suggests death is nigh.

The barmaid at the Salmon is a lady of the classical proportions of her trade, and after she'd overcome her fear of the unusual she said she would take the lamb within her ample cardigan, if that would help to warm the lamb up.

And this kind offer had a strange effect on the discussion group. At once the boys were showing all the signs which, in a lamb, would have suggested hypothermia. They were stretching their heads backwards in a pathetic quest for warmth. I may say that none was forthcoming though, by the side of the roaring log fire, the lamb did appear to perk up.

Still the prognosis was not good. And when the pub cat came to investigate the strange bundle by the fire, Potions told him, with unnecessary courseness I thought, "That's just Kit-e-Kat without the tin."

I fear he may have been right.

April 18, 1994

Mossie sells out of pure public spirit

I AM sorry to have to tell you that the lambie died, despite the kind attentions of the barmaid in the snug at the Salmon Inn. She took the two day old lamb to her bosom. It seemed to help for a while, but two days later it was dead.

And so to the good news. Mossie is selling Moss-side.

Mind you, it is not the home farm of Moss-side of Tarves that he's selling. That is his family seat, and there was a tear in his eye only a year ago when he managed to liberate it from the insurance company who had bought it in the bad old days of the 1980s - when Aberdeenshire was described in the agricultural press as 'A County for Sale!'.

At least, I think it was a tear. It may have been a glint for, having sold it as a freeholder and leased it back, he was able to buy his heritage back again as a sitting tenant at half price or less (depending on how hard he is blawing).

No, no. Mossie is selling his out-farm of Moss-side of Gight. He added that to his empire after the disastrous harvests in the late 1980s, when the white settlers were being bussed into the North-east. Land was cheap then, and you might think that it was the current boom in land prices, and the prospect of profit, that was now provoking the sale.

Nothing could be farther from the truth. Mossie is selling out of pure public spirit. He explained it to me over a couple of pints on Sunday.

"Aabody keeps saying, 'You farmers have it easy. You canna possibly fail with all those subsidies. You get paid to grow nothing, and you get a fortune if you do grow anything on your farms. You're just a lot of under-aged, feather-bedded, state pensioners.' Well this is the chance for them to come and try it. This farm is all eligible for set-aside. They can buy it and set it all aside and get £120 pounds an acre for it. At 250 acres, that's £30,000 for nothing, the way they see it. This is their chance to find out just how easy it is. And if that's nae enough for them, they can grow some of these big-sub-

sidy crops, and they'll maybe find that's easy tae."

"If they dinna buy this farm, they've missed their chance - and they'll have to shut up."

I found out about the sale when I saw him out with the sprayer. It has been a very late season here, on the southern edge of the ancient Thanage of Buchan, and most of the fields were, until the last few days, still showing their brown winter coats. I went over to see what Mossie was spraying because, even from here, you could see his farm shining green.

"Well, to tell you the truth Charlie, I'm desperate to have her looking her best for the sale, and I've just filled the sprayer wi green paint. What a success, isn't it?"

He's definitely out to trap a settler. He's knocked down the old steading, despite how handy it was for storing old bicycles, empty fire extinguishers and bundles of second-hand bags, just to give the house a look at the rolling countryside to the south.

"I see you've left the shed you used to fatten 1000 pigs in, though," I said. After the money that has been lost in pigs over the last eight months, I should have known not to mention it.

Mossie looked at me with surprise, bordering at once on

disdain and hurt. "That is the indoor equestrian facility," he said, grandly.

"How much are you expecting an acre, Mossie?" said I, as though there was the slightest danger of him telling me the truth.

"Fifteen hunder, and not a penny less - unless I canna help it."

I was staggered. You don't get farms called Moss-side of anywhere without they have bits that are best for snipe-shooting. "You're surely nae wantin fifteen hunder for that wet hole over the back," says I.

"That's more!" he squealed in indignation. "That's my FENland. That's three thoosand pound an acre in England so it must be worth at least that in Buchan.

"In fact, de ye ken this Charlie," he enthused at last, with even more than his usual modesty, "I've made the place such a show, I'm thinkin o' puttin in a bid masel."

There is little doubt Mossie would get his price if he were selling some of the fat lands of the Mearns where, as I told you, the Breadwinner and I dined recently among the farming aristocracy. That's the rich red land upon which my uncle George once exclaimed, "any fool could farm here."

At that dinner, I particulary enjoyed listening to other farmers trying to get the better of their neighbours.

Like John Forbes of Slains Park near Stonehaven, who was very hard on Ian Stirling who farms extensively around Dundee. Forbes was anxious to make the point that Stirling's farming was antiquated. So out of date was he, that he wouldn't have minded that, every fifteen years he needed a new dairyman, if he didn't have to buy a new graip as well.

I don't blame him. Have you seen the price of a thirty-bob graip recently?

And what of my farming among all that chatter?

The calves keep appearing and, with the exception of a quite unexpected death of one seemingly thriving ten-day-old heifer, they keep living - after the odd anxious moment. I now have 31 calves from 30 cows, and need a further 8.6 calves for a full house on my quota.

And I am all set for the pay-off on last year's maternity. Tomorrow I send 21 heifers to Maud Market. The banker is making contingency plans to invest the expected cheque, and my creditors are hovering.

Next week I'll tell you (truthfully) how I got on.

Ringing up at the back door

THERE ARE two things the Breadwinner hates about life here on the hill of my ancestors. One of them is when Mossie phones up and she spends most of Coronation Street trying to hear a word, as I bawl down the phone about what's gone wrong with Hillie's wheat - or when we should put the Butisan on the spring rape.

So, when the great man, Thousand Acre Club branch president, and honorary crop consultant phoned on Saturday, I moved through to the front room to speak to him and leave the wife in peace - for there was much to discuss.

There was the wedding of the year for a start. The landlady at the Salmon has decided to make an honest man of the landlord, and that's a fair contract for a start. Mossie had done all the cooking of beef, pork, and turkey on his smiddy-built mobile spit-roaster, so that had to be praised lavishly if a row was to be avoided.

Then there was all that food and drink, and the fact that the best man just read out a few of the telegrams and forgot that he was supposed to toast the bridesmaid.

We agreed that the bride had decorated the old village hall to a picture, and that it had really been a lovely ceremony - and great fun. But how had we all got back to the Salmon Inn afterwards, and how came it that we broke open another whole porker at two o'clock in the morning?

Mossie says he saw me in a disorientated state at three thirty, a time when he, he swears, was cold sober.

Clearly one of us was disorientated, for I am absolutely certain I arrived home at two thirty (I always take careful note so I can take off an hour when the Breadwinner wants to know the next morning). And if he was so damned sober, where did he get the hangover he had complained of?

We both agreed that the happy couple had given us a great do, as well as plenty to speak about in the weeks to come. But we couldn't agree with their choice of honeymoon. The next day they were catering at the Salmon for a party of 150 for shooting and then dinner with a late licence.

They must be, in Mossie's immortal words, "the workin fools".

Anyway, after we'd got the best of the chat over I asked him where he was phoning from. "I'm just at your back door. Can I come in? It's awful cauld oot here."

This craze for mobile phones started off as a pose. It was all sorts of people's idea of having made it, to drive a white Range-Rover with a mobile phone stuck to their ear. In that phase I think Potions, the local chemist, had it about right. He bought himself a plastic play phone for £3.40, just one percent of the price of a real one. It did just as well for driving along posing, it was much safer, and the calls were free.

But now the mobile phone seems to be for real. I don't like it. You can't get a sensible conversation from Crookie and the Red Rooster. As soon as you get going, one or other of them will get a call from someone in Cambridge who has a rather interesting one-pass machine to sell.

Even Potions has a real phone now. Whenever I've got him going mucking a byre or rolling a park, the mobile rings. The shop has run out of aspirins and he has to go for more..

WHERE YE PHONING FROM?

MOSSIE THE POSER!

AH'M AT YER BACK DOOR!

142

I suppose I'll have to give in and join them, but I don't like it.

And I don't like people who are always having bad luck at the mart. I just don't believe in bad luck. When it comes to marketing stock there is no luck, just management.

So the events at Maud market this week went particularly hard with me. I had rotten luck. Everything that could be done wrong was done wrong, and everything that could go wrong did.

First, I decided there would be no need to take my twenty heifer calves down to the loading bank. They would load out of the shed door. I was right of course, but what a struggle! My carefully prepared heifers were not looking any the better of the fight when we did finally raise the tail-door.

To fit in with the rest of his work, the floater insisted that my cattle go to market two hours before they were due through the ring. That's two hours of digestive activity and no eating. It can cost you ten kilos per head. But the mart made a poor job of estimating my time of sale and, instead of half past one, mine weren't sold until four. Bang, swish, plot went another ten kilos of liveweight.

And at least as bad was my luck in the draw for when the cattle are sold. I was last into the ring. The buyers had been there for six hours when it came to my turn. Or they would have, if they hadn't all gone home.

Well, they hadn't ALL gone home. There were my two pals and three dealers.

If that wasn't enough to ensure a disaster, they were badly drawn. The showiest Simmental heifer I've ever bred was put into the ring as a pair with a screw with a humpy back. I had four calves out of my Hereford-Friesian heifers and by the Angus bull (remember old Rastus?) which were just too small for the sale. They should have been at the little ring at Thainstone, not at the mighty Maud market.

I do not know why I didn't call a halt and bring them home for sale another day, but I can't do it now. They averaged a whisker less than 130 pence a kilo, and remember there was no liveweight about them at all. They must have been the most concentrated cattle in the sale.

I've thirty-five born for next year - when I promise to do better.

May 2, 1994

Just no luck with steers either

ONCE UPON a time there was a cattle dealer who made a living that was more or less honest out of buying cattle where they were cheap, and selling them where they were dear. On this occasion, places where they were cheap seemed to outnumber the places where they were dear, so the dealer had done more buying than selling for a week or two. An overdraft emerged and then grew.

As bankers will, the banker phoned the dealer and invited him for a £50 interview to discuss the situation.

There were few of the little civilities that would have been common twenty years ago. There was no messing with, "How's Mrs Dealer?" just a curt, "terrible weather", and the banker was off into his lecture on thrift and the need to make prior arrangements for borrowing money "in today's climate."

As is best with paper tigers when they are in high dudgeon, Dealer let the banker blow his indignation out, and then took his turn.

"And how much is my

144

overdraft?"

"Sixteen thousand, seven hundred and twenty pounds, and fourteen pence," said the banker.

"And how much was it last month?"

"Oh well, last month you were in a surplus of twenty-five thousand."

"And did I phone you?" enquired Mr Dealer with force.

Unfortunately, my informant could not tell me how the banker responded to that one.

I tell you that little story, which might not be strictly true but has some truth in it, because it illustrates the problems we farmers face when our best laid schemes go wrong.

And the other schemes go wrong as well. Once again I have made a mess of my financial planning and must throw myself on the brutal mercy of the bankers. It will be a total humiliation too, I'm afraid.

This spring when I got the usual letter to go and see Sir about renegotiating my overdraft facility, I just couldn't bear to pay £50 for another cup of Nescafe. I decided to do without an overdraft facility, let alone an overdraft. I thought I could just see my way through to harvest if I sold all my young stock onto the grass, and then did a little bit of prevarication over some of my bills.

I sold the heifers last week and, as I told you, that went poorly. Still, all would be well if I could get a flier for the steers this week.

I had no such luck. If you are one of those who thinks farmers can't go wrong with all the subsidies we get, you can take up Mossie's challenge and buy the farm he's selling and find out for yourself. But it might pay you to read this first.

Nowadays, male beef cattle have passports with the romantic name 'CCDs'. My calves are eligible for a subsidy when they are eight months old, and another when they are twenty-one months old. My cash flow is carefully planned round taking the first subsidy and then selling as soon as possible. To get the subby you've got to register the calves, and they send you a white CCD for each. Then you've got to send the white CCD back to the Department, and they will send you back a blue CCD - and a cheque.

What could be simpler? It is foolproof.

No. Not really.

Last year, you applied for the CCD and the first subby in one fell swoop. I did that this year and prepared to receive my £1400 for my twenty steers. None has come, and when I looked out the passports to send them to the mart on Friday, I

145

could see from reading the CCD that something was wrong. I have to apply for a blue passport, and keep my steers for another two months, if I want my £1400 - and I do.

All that leaves a hole (£12,000 deep and two months long) in my cash flow. And that's not counting the £50 to the banker for the cup of Nescafe.

When you have a hundred beasts, only four bales of silage and twenty bales of straw, and the grass is just beginning to turn green, it is no joke to find you have to keep twenty big steers extra.

And it could have been worse - a lot worse.

I found that I had twenty-one CCDs and filled up the form to claim the lot. That was a mistake which might have cost me a small fortune. In the charmingly named "AICS" system, I have undertaken to jump through various hoops to get an additional subsidy for farming extensively. Indeed, it appears that I have only enough acres here to claim for twenty steers. I was told quite unambiguously that, had I claimed for the extra steer, I'd have lost all my subbies - and that's a five figure sum.

I tell you this subsidy farming is not as easy as it looks.

I'm sorry I can't give you an update on the sale of Moss-side of Gight, which figured in last week's cartoon. Mossie has come over all coy about what sort of response there has been to the sale so far. It's a bit like those countries where they won't allow opinion polls in the last few weeks before an election. As closing day for Moss-side approaches, the curtains have come down.

I don't know whether there has been anybody or nobody to see it, but there are some clues. There has been a lot of traffic on the road to Gight. It has been standing room only on the Larne to Stranraer Ferry. And, though Mossie has been tight-lipped in one sense, he has been shipping a hellova lot of barley - and smiling a lot.

One bound, and they were free

MY FATHER used to say that he could hear the grass grow in a warm day in May. It is good to be a farmer at this time of year.

It's good to be a cow too. Nothing makes cows grow, puts milk into their calves, or makes them come on heat and thrive, like the sun on their backs.

After a winter which has been much longer than average, we've got most of them out to what our vet calls "Dr Green."

And the weather has been just perfect for the turnout. If you turn the beasts out onto wet pasture, they are liable to take a bellyful of this low fibre diet and blow up to their discomfort - and even death.

If it is wet they will, as they say, "eat with five mouths" as they parade round and round, turning a delicate sward into a darkening mud-bath that will never be grass, though it may eventually turn green.

There have been no such problems this year.

By buying silage I have held onto them until the grass is ready, and they have all gone out on fine dry days.

That doesn't mean all has gone smoothly. It has not.

As a one-man band, I have to play things cunning to get help in putting the beasts out. One or two can be allowed to run after I have shut all the relevant gates and blocked various leaky bits with diggers, tractors and cars.

Others can go when Potions appears. Luckily, he gets about as excited as the cattle at turn-out so he is often about.

But there are some journeys which cannot be done without more staff. They don't know it yet, but it is for that reason that we have instituted a family tradition called 'brunch.' On Sunday we have ham and eggs and all the trimmings for the family and their children.

This weekend we had eleven. We even had the Wasting Asset. He usually can't make it because one o'clock is a bit too early in the morning, and it's uphill from his cottage on the brae. The Recovery Stock was there too. His restaurant is doing so well that he no longer fears having to work

on the farm, and was willing to give me a 'kepp' as I steered the stotties down to the park beside the road - there is no point in holding onto last year's calves without flaunting such wealth to all the passers-by. After all, they don't know that it was because I forgot to get my forms up to date.

There were two weak points on the route. The Recovery Stock would make sure they went down the brae and not into the first field of wheat. The Wasting Asset would guard the next wheatfield, Potions would make sure they turned left at the main road, and the Investment would turn them into the Waterside park.

Unfortunately, half the stots decided they'd rather not leave the shed, so we were left with two herds of cattle - and still just the one ropey crew.

When the first lot came charging down through the close the Recovery Stock, who is fresh from running the London Marathon, abandoned his post and went charging after them. When I came along with the second half, there was no stopping them. One bound - and they were free.

Except that He who looks after those who try hard in difficult circumstances, smiled once more on this sinner. Instead of making for the wide open wheatfields, they ran to speak to the two cows and three calves in the looseboxes. That gave me time to get round behind them, and steer them down the hill to fresh fields and pastures new.

When I got my little herd down to the second potential trouble-spot, the two heroes were deep in discussion in the middle of the road. The cattle could have been forgiven for thinking that the two boys were there to stop them going any further.

They all stopped, and started looking for escape routes - as I yelled to my helpers to get to hell back and let the stots see the gate.

I was in time for all but one of them. He's been in the wheat, the rape, and over to have a look at the wood, before jumping in amongst some cows. He's happy there and the Farmer isn't at all unhappy to have got ninety-five percent of the cattle out to the right field.

It really is uncanny how Mossie can spot trouble at Little Ardo. It is also incredible how much he hates cattle. It is true that before he became so good at the crops, he too spent much time chasing cattle, and going to see the banker about putting shelvings on his overdraft.

Anyway, no sooner had we got the wanderer settled than Mossie appeared, delighted to see we'd been having trouble again. "Of course, you have to hide the money someway. What a tax that stotties must be saving you! That's the way forward, I can see," he said with heavy irony.

Mind you, it is getting easier. Indeed, we have just invested £250 in what I believe is a wonderful labour-saving device.

For the last twenty summers I've spent at least an hour every second day carrying drums of magnesium syrup (without which they get staggers) to my cows in the field.

Not this time though. Gazzer, the blacksmith, is making another fortune for himself out of a new feeder. The cattle lick the stuff off two-feet-diameter wheels, and the only fear is that they might not have enough power in their tongues to drag the syrup up from the bottom. We won't know about that until the feeder is nearly empty, but in the meantime I have taken a thousand litres down to the field on the fork lift. I won't even have to look at it for a month.

Busman's holiday for Argus

THE IMMACULATE births keep on and on. We put the bull in for only six weeks, and yet we have had calves being born for nine weeks - and there may be three still to come.

At one time I'd have said it was just that one of the young bulls we used to breed had jumped the dyke. Or, more likely, a very young bull had got to one of his half-sisters when he was supposed to be still in short breeks.

But nowadays we have no young bulls about the place, and the bull calves are castrated before they can jump to advantage. And these late calves can't be the work of any neighbouring bulls. We only have one neighbour still using live bulls, and they have so much work to do at home - and so far to come - that I can't see them sneaking up on any that our Argus has missed.

Our other neighbours use the bull with the bowler hat, as we used to call the AI man, or borrow Argus. In fact he's away down to Gowkie's at the moment on a busman's holiday, getting his eye in for serving our mamas from the first of June.

Although it has lasted for nine weeks already, this is definitely my best calving. So far, we have forty-one calves from forty cows. We have just lost one twin, and she was so healthy looking that I can't help feeling that she was always going to die. I have only treated one calf for pneumonia and one for scour (and it wasn't needing it).

The young laird, who has no use for the money it will bring him anyway, has also had a calving percentage of over a hundred. He has had three sets of twins and two deaths. Embarrassingly, one of those occurred the day he agreed to look round the beasts in the morning, to let the cattleman help in the potato planting.

Next day, the cattleman turned up in a barely-controlled rage, saying that he had found a dead calf in the field, and it was damned funny that there had been no sign the day before when the boss had allegedly been in control. The poor young laird, whose up-bringing has left him quite unequipped for telling barefaced lies, had to admit that he had just driven round in his Range-Rover, and hadn't even done a count.

And young Ochyoch has had his problems though, over all, he has done well too. He had twenty heifers, and was sailing towards a full house when he lost the last calf. Mind

Now, as I have told you, young Ochyoch is a rare and tender plant, who is to be encouraged - and whose misfortunes should touch us all. When his manager's job disappeared he put all his savings and all he could get out of several banks into 350 acres of rented ground. He farms that in his spare time, after milking someone else's cows. And better than that, he has three

DON'T FANCY HIM MUCH !

you, all was not lost.

The heifers had been bought from a dealer and were guaranteed in calf to the Aberdeen-Angus bull. But this last one was so late, and was so obviously by a Charolais, that the dealer agreed to provide a replacement.

sons to follow him.

So Ochyoch has to be careful. When he loses a calf he doesn't just bung a new calf in with the cow, and teach her that when she kicks the calf, a heavy stick descends on her back.

No, no. Young Ochyoch left nothing to chance.

151

While the dead calf was still warm, it was skinned. The idea was to put the new calf inside the old calf's skin and thereby fool the mother into thinking it was her own calf reincarnate.

I am told that plan works well with sheep, and that it can work with cattle. But not this time.

The cow was not so easily fooled. She showed absolutely no interest in the strange bundle of calf skin she was being offered.

And no wonder. The replacement calf was, in Ochyoch's words "an affa lookin reptile o' a thing". Indeed, so small and phlegmatic was the calf that it either could not, or would not, get up and challenge the cows udder. It just lay there in it's macabre overcoat, and drifted off towards death.

Ochyoch's sense of humour was sorely tried. He phoned the dealer and told him to look out a second replacement, and make sure it was bigger and stronger than the second, and a lot less dead than the original.

In a fit of disgust tinged with remorse, young Ochyoch took the shaggy and smelly coat off the calf and went to leave him to his maker.

But then a funny thing happened. Released from the burden of the great hide, the calf struggled to its feet and made unsteadily for its foster mother. She was delighted, and proceeded to lick away all trace of the smelly outer skin from which the calf had been liberated.

Of course, the calf is still a screw but at least now it is a healthy screw.

It's D day for Mossie in the sale of his outfarm, but I can't get through to him to see if there was anything in his snares. He set so many, he might have scared them off. Certainly his technique of telling buyers that he was sure of at least one offer, because he had put in a hefty bid himself could have put some people off.

If he has sold, it will not be without regret. He told me on Sunday that he was thinking of applying to the Beechgrove Garden for a job because, with 250 acres less, he would just be down to garden-sized.

They'll let him stay in the Thousand Acre Club though, if it's only for the laughs.

Mossie plays the field

MOSSIE HAS sold his farm - maybe. When he looked at his snares last Tuesday, there were five bids - not including his own. And, oh boy! Is he enjoying the fact that we would all like to know how much he got for it and who the buyer is?

"How much did you get then, Moss?"

"Ye ken this boys. It's nae the money ye get. It goes against the grain to sell land. If ye're brought up on the soil it is like selling the family silver to sell land even at twa thoosand an acre - not that that was what Moss-side made, mind you."

"Get away, Mossie. That wasna even YOUR family silver you were selling. You bought that place ten years ago when land was cheap and now that it is dear you're selling to make a profit."

"Maybe so. But when I realised that my bid was far too low to keep the farm, there was a lump in my throat. Aye, boys, it brought a tear tae my eye right enough. Of course I could maybe remember just how much the successful bid was if I had anither pint."

"And was it one o the Irishmen that got it Moss?"

"Aye, aye. It could have been right enough, but I canna say yet. Discretion boys, ye ken."

Mossie normal is bad enough, but Mossie coy about priceless information is just ridiculous.

At any rate it is clear that those owner-occupiers among us are rich and the tenants can forget those plans for expansion. Land hereabouts on the southern tip of Buchan is making £1500 an acre and maybe more. What it will be worth in five years time, with what is likely to happen to the EC subsidies, is only going to be of academic interest to me as I retire then and, the farm belonging to my family rather than to me, I won't be selling it anyway.

But what a reflection this boom in land prices is on the professionals. I refer to those who, because of their expertise in financial matters, make a good living off investing the pension money of workers, widows and orphans. What a boon they have been to so many farmers.

When the price of land was high in the early eighties, something like a third of the farmers about here sold out to the insurance companies and pension funds. Interest rates were high then and it made very good sense for the boys to sell and put the money in the bank to bring the overdraft down to reasonable proportions.

And it didn't mean they were finished as farmers. The professionals who knew so much about money knew nothing about farming, and were happy to let the farmers stay on as tenants. The net effect was that, instead of paying up to 20 percent to the banks, farmers were able to pay about 4 percent to their landlords.

You may think that a good deal for the farmers, and so it was, but it turned out to be far better than anyone could have thought.

In the late eighties, the price of land collapsed. With all this talk of eliminating EC subsidies, the future looked glum and the professionals panicked and decided to sell. Soon they were selling at any price. All the farmers hereabout were offered the chance to buy their farms back at half the price they had got for them.

Typically, they sold for about a thousand pounds an acre, sat on a rent of 4 percent for ten years and then bought back for five hundred. And that's the experts for you. I'm glad I haven't got experts like that looking after my pension. They are supposed to be looking after their clients' money, not supporting Scotland's farmers, but they don't seem to realise that. They haven't even realised that the way to make money is to buy cheap and sell dear.

Mossie hit the nail on the head the other day when he met one of the financial wizards who were buying up the land in Aberdeenshire the last time it was dear. "Wi land at fifteen hunder pound an acre, is it nae time you pension fund boys were buyin again?"

I hear some of them are in the market already, but others will likely wait till it goes a bit higher. The chances are, land hasn't peaked yet.

And it's not just the sale of his outfarm that Mossie is being secretive about. He doesn't like anybody to know what he's putting on his crops. That could lead to problems when he is advising me, but he reckons I am too thick to figure out what he is doing. I have to be very

154

careful to foster the image of the daft laddie with whom his secrets are quite safe.

I was reminded sharply of that truth this week.

He was giving me a list of chemicals to put in a magic brew for the winter wheat when, in all innocence, I asked if one particular chemical was to help the Scramrot to work on the Rhincosporium..

In an instant he was at my throat. "Never you mind what it's for. Your job is to write it doon, get it on, and keep yer mou shut."

I'm sorry I can't tell you the final outcome of the sale of Moss-side of Gight. Believe me I would tell all if I knew it. But I thought you might like this true tale of Mossie, the farm salesman.

Our man was showing a victim round at the stage when the snares were still being set. He had a painter there to paint the roan pipes. Mossie excused himself for a moment to speak to the tradesman, who wanted to know what colour to paint them.

"Hold on a minute," said Mossie and, to the prospective buyer, "What colour are you needin your spouts painted?"

Mossie takes a hammering

THERE IS an apocryphal story, told often in Aberdeenshire, about a farmer who was asked how he was getting on. "Oh nae sae bad, really. In fact I think the money will last, as lang as I dinna live ower lang." I know it's bad form to admit it, but things are going even better than that on the top of Ardo's hill. There is no chance of the profit getting up to the dizzy heights of what they tell us is the average industrial wage these days. But what would I do with £400 a week? I'd never have the time to spend that kind of money.

But, unlike throughout most of my farming life, there is now a clear indication of profit.

The mainstay of this unusual situation is a set of unusual circumstances. All the crops are doing well. There isn't a single wet hole, slug damaged, tory-eaten, chemical-spilled, weed drowned, or missed bit on the whole farm.

Or so you would think if I took you on a conducted tour. In fact, I killed quite a bit of winter rape at the endriggs because I wasn't quite up to the controls of my new tractor. And there are a couple of fields of wheat which are a bit thin because the slugs got every second plant. But you'd never see them as I sped you past.

I'm not confident that it is a good thing for the environment, but one of the mainstays of all that well-being is the fact that we are not keeping any weeds this year. Mossie and I were in a field of barley the other day and he offered me a pound a weed. I looked everywhere and couldn't find one. Not, that is, until I went out to the field's edge. "Here's one," says I, but he wouldn't pay.

"Na, na. If I let ye away wi that, you'd be away up to Hillies and bringin weeds back in handfuls."

Mains says our success is because we've poured on so many chemicals that there is a special hole on the ozone layer over Little Ardo, and that has let in a whole lot of sunshine.

But that can't really be it. When I was being advised by

156

an expert crops adviser, and had expert sprayers putting the stuff on, we spent over forty pounds an acre on sprays and once got over fifty. But, now that Mossie is on for honorary. spray adviser and I'm doing the spraying myself, I am down to thirty pounds an acre. I do more spraying, but seem to get away with less chemical rather than more.

So there must be some other reason for the sunshine. By the end of the first week in May we had already had more sunshine than in the whole of the 1993 growing season. Then, we only had four days of sunshine all summer.

We didn't like to admit it, but we were all impressed at Mossie managing to grow that crop of sunflowers so far north and without even our normal wintry sun. So, with all the sun this year, what sort of a crop will he grow?

Well, the answer to that one is awaited with interest but a great deal of uncertainty. It appears that yellow hammers have a passion for sunflower shoots. No sooner were the little cotyledons peeping up through the ground, than the bush telegraph was buzzing and every "yalla yitie", as we call them in the North-east, was setting a course for Moss-side.

There was a time when we farmers were the kings of the countryside. Mossie's father would have invited a few friends round for a couple of days' shooting, and the problem would have been solved at a cost to Aberdeenshire of nothing more than a shortage of yellow hammers.

But farmers are no longer kings, or even lords of what is their own. Mossie had no sooner yoked the twelve-bore than he felt a pair of spyglasses on him. It was one of the white settlers from across the moss taking an unhealthy interest in his pest control.

Mossie was astonished when I told him he should check the legality of shooting yellow hammers with the RSPB. Sure enough, he was told that yellow hammers cannot be shot because they aren't a pest species.

"It is easy to see it's nae your sunflooers the little beggars are eatin," cried the injured farmer. "And how much is the fine anyway?"

"It's a thousand pounds per bird you shoot - or try to shoot."

"But there's thoosands o' them," said Mossie as his brain got to work like an angry computer. That means to say I could face a fine of millions of pounds, just for sheetin a few yalla yities?"

"Yes indeed, sir. I hope I

157

have been of some help."

"Some help!"

But that was Mossie's problem.

The nearest I've had to a problem was the indignity suffered at a commercial clay-pigeon shoot the other day. It was given by a company called Field Engineering Services which supply drinking bowls and such accessories for pigs kept out in the fields instead of in factories where they belong.

At the prize-giving I was shocked when the chairman held up a rather attractive leather-bound book and said. "We have a difficult job each year finding something absolutely useless for a booby prize, but this year we've scored. It's Farmer's Diary, Volume Two, by Charlie Allan."

That was greeted by a burst of rather unkind applause. And worse than that, they hadn't even bought it. It was the copy I had given Mossie for his Christmas.

No reply to the mobile

THERE AREN'T many moments of drama at agricultural shows, but there is one when the judge in the cattle rings has his final short leet drawn up before him. He knows exactly which beast he is going to place first, but this is pure theatre. The learned judge struts up and down the line, checking carefully the conformation on the udder of the cow with calf at foot, comparing the heights for age of the junior and senior heifers, and generally putting on a show.

Then after much simulated heart-searching, this man (for it is usually such) is suddenly quite sure that there is a clear winner. He signifies his choice by striding confidently forward and slapping the winner firmly on the rump.

It is a breathless moment. Or it should be.

Last Saturday, I was that man at the great Strathendrick Agricultural Society's Show at Drymen. Once more, I was more than a hundred miles away from home and therefore an expert whose advice is sought on matters which, at home, I would admit are a mystery.

I had the job of lining up the Blondes d'Aquitaine, which was a less exciting job than it sounds as none turned up, and the Charolais.

But it was when I was at the moment of truth among the Simmentals that I was assaulted by a clash of cultures. The ancient rituals of the show ring were rudely interrupted by brash modernism.

Just as I was stepping forward with my mind made up, there was a ringing from one of those infernal mobile telephones. The cattleman to whom I was about to make the award reached into his white coat, produced the offending machine, and proceeded to roar into it.

"Jist haud oan boys. It's a call from my broker. Pork bellies are falling on the Chicago futures market."

Naturally I was furious, as my moment for being so important was hijacked. I whipped out my mobile and tried to get in the queue to speak to the

young man but, unfortunately, he hasn't got a queueing facility.

I wonder if Stephen Wilson (for such was his name) got one of his pals to phone him up at the crucial point just to put the judge in his place. Certainly it is just about as good a pose as you'll get.

It's just the sort of stunt my pals in Aberdeenshire would pull. Indeed, one such is being pulled as I write.

Mossie, as you know, has just beaten the Buchan record price for selling a farm. And his patient wife, Alison, has booked them a holiday in Spain so that she can recover from her husband's excitement.

Mossie doesn't often go from home, and it is a good chance for a wind-up. Twenty of the lads, led by the Red Rooster, Crookie and Butcher Bain, have run a series of adverts in the Spanish newspapers. I haven't seen them yet, but the theme is something like this:

El Opportunidad Fantastico! Following the successful sale of their estates in Buchan, Moss-side Enterprises are looking for investment opportunities in Ibiza. Anything legal considered. Some time-share blocks essential. Apply Dr Mossie, who is in residence at Siccansick Hotel. Best before lunch.

I'll tell you next week what he was offered, if it's fit to print.

But back to the Show on that beautiful site on the banks of the Endrick at Drymen.

160

It was a great day, and fine to be away from the home midden. At one time you would have had to be down the night before, but nowadays you can do the beasts, drive 150 miles and be in plenty of time for the judging at half-past nine.

I met a lot of friendly folk, including one who roared at me: "Did ye no bring the Money-Spinner wi ye?" I presumed he was asking about the Breadwinner and told him, truthfully, that she doesn't come often with me. She doesn't like to leave her spindle for long.

And I saw a few ferlies.

When I arrived I thought the lucky devils of Strathendrick had had a shower of rain - but no. They had just wet all the roads to keep down the stour. What a change from last year. Already we've had twice the sunshine we had the whole of last summer and, while a suppy rain would be gratefully received, the job is easier in the sun.

Then I met my first show chairman wearing denim. She's Lorna MacWilliam, the first lady in the job. She looked so cool in her outfit from Nashville, that I decided it was time I stopped putting on the country gentleman suit I got at Oxfam, and turned out in something more country-western. What are ties supposed to do, apart from restrict the blood supply to the brain?

There was a great show of Limousin cattle, because Drymen is one of their qualifying events for 'Herd of the Year'. They far out-numbered the Herefords, which are the biggest breed in the world, and the Charolais and Simmentals which dominate in the UK.

Then there were no goats. How can you have an agricultural show with no goats? Is Strathendrick not settler country? Some of our shows would have shut down years ago if it hadn't been for the goat section.

Well, apparently they were over-run with goats ten years ago. Now the fashion has changed - to Shetland sheep, for one. There were grand big classes there and plenty of enthusiasm, especially from Emma Douglas of the breed Society.

But mostly now, it's horse. It was grand to see a class of ten Clydesdale geldings, but all those toy horses - I caused a few sighs when I told them that at my local show in Buchan the toys are banished to another field. We do drive past them when we arrive, but you can't have everything.

Farewell to our old grieve

THERE WE were, in this church - some bits of which were there in the twelfth century - roaring away about building Jerusalem in England's green and pleasant land. We also sang the Lord's My Shepherd to the tune 'Crimond'. It was a strange thing to see so many North-east farmers, some in their kilts, in Essex on a day when they might have been at the silage. And yet, the whole thing was just as it should be.

I had had to rise at four to get round the beasts, feed them (yes, we are that short of grass), and catch the plane to Stansted for the funeral of John Mackie.

Now, I wouldn't like you to think that I rig myself out for the funeral of every Minister for Agriculture. But Mackie was grieve at Little Ardo when he was sixteen. He made the crystal set with which my mother broke all the rules at Miss Oliver's Boarding School for Girls by listening, heads under the covers with her pal Ella Anderson, to the music from the Palm Court Hotel.

He also used to scare me somewhat by enquiring, with his eyes over the top of his spectacles, why the hell I wasn't outside playing.

The Crimond tune was appropriate for the funeral of my uncle John, because it was composed in Aberdeenshire about twenty miles from where he was brought up, the son of the tenant of 400 second class acres.

Jerusalem was fitting too, though in less obvious ways.

John Mackie was an enthusiast and (though he would not have agreed) an idealist. He didn't see farming merely as a way of putting shoes on the bairns' feet and paying for the booze. He saw the proper use of land as the means to banish toil and to banish hunger.

John Boyd-Orr, the director of the Rowett Institute, had shown that the hungry thirties were just a case of mismanagement by feeding the British better than they had ever been fed before, despite the difficulties imposed by the war. The generation that grew during the war years were a good inch taller, ricketts disappeared, and the farmers made a good living.

And John Mackie was determined that the same sort of good management could be applied to hunger on a world scale. There was no need for shortage if the job were done right. Every mechanical advance was eagerly embraced on his farms in the Howe o' the Mearns, later in Lincolnshire, and finally in Essex.

When he became a minister in Harold Wilson's government, John Mackie was able to pursue agricultural efficiency on the grand scale. He was able, at last, to get Charolais cattle in from Europe to produce more lean meat for less input. And he pushed through the Amalga- mation Scheme, whereby farmers of uneconomic units were paid to retire, provided they sold to neighbours. And the neighbours were given money to facilitate the consolidation of farms into bigger units.

But John Mackie's attempts to build Jerusalem are floundering still, and they are floundering among some irony. Like the fact that this socialist, who was among the first to see in the 1930s that the tractor was the way forward, lived to see the day when his beautiful farm, which was called Harold's Park after a previous Royal owner, would have no other livestock than the horses of the well-to-do in Essex.

And then there is the irony of set-aside. Ian Aitken of the

Guardian, in his eulogy for our old grieve, put it like this: John Mackie was like a high priest of a fundamentalist religion, which believed that the only thing that really mattered was making things people wanted, and that the most important thing of all was the production of food. "That is why he was so angry and depressed by Europe paying farmers NOT to produce food. He regarded as an abomination the deliberate refusal to produce food in a world in which millions were starving. It is perhaps one of the saddest features of his final years that he saw even his precious acres at Harold's Park being forced by government policy into non-productive uses."

But John Mackie never wavered from the view that there was no indelible shortage of food in the world, just bad distribution. Even during the last days of his battle with the Great Reaper, he was taken up with the problem. He was very upset about the current suffering in Rwanda. It was in recognition of that worry that a collection was taken at the funeral for relief there.

The selflessness of that brought tears to the Farmer's eyes.

And there was more to provoke a sentimental tear in the valedictory letter my uncle left.

Although a former minister, and as a sequence a reluctant Peer of the Realm, John Mackie had no desire for pomp at his funeral. He refused to have a hearse near the place.

He left instructions that his box (for it was not coffin shaped) should travel in the cart that he and the blacksmith at Bent of Laurencekirk had made in 1935. And, as is the tradition of some on Scotland's east coast, he was taken (behind a Ford 7610) round the farm "for a last look" and down through the Essex countryside to the church where he now lies.

The driver was his son George who had had a few sleepless nights. Everyone who has ever driven a tractor will know how easy it is to shift the handle and find that you are driving along with a tipped cart. He must be sure that would not happen this day. So George disconnected the hydraulic pipe just in case. And just in further case some kind person stuck it back in for him, he tied the pipe firmly back, as far from the connection as possible.

When I got home to Little Ardo all was as well as when I left that morning, and the last cow had calved, a fine pure Simmental bull.

164

Barley gets unexpected compliment

THE EXCITEMENT is rising as we sweep towards a bounteous harvest. Things are looking really well. Something dreadful must be about to happen but, in the meantime, I am going to enjoy my crops looking as they have seldom looked before.

Mossie is excited about them too. He even brought the Red Rooster to look and to wonder. They've always been good at looking. But they are not so good at showing wonder, and less than generous in expressing it.

Mind you, I was nervous when I saw them, bums in the air like a pair of enormous peasant women weeding, giving the barley a once-over on

Thursday. The Rooster, whose shock of red hair is mellowing to a gentler rustie colour, but is still growing well despite a life lived to the overflowing, unfolded himself and, from his full six feet four, shook his head and said: "Well Charlie, you've proved aa the experts wrang. Your jets are knackered, you've nae idea what pressure you're spraying at, you dinna even know what varieties of seeds you've sown, and yet you've the cleanest barley in Aberdeenshire."

That counts as a compliment hereabouts, but that stuff about not knowing what seeds I had sown was very unkind. I knew he was standing in a field of 'Winter Barley' for a start.

Anyway, I'll suffer the slings and arrows if it turns out to be a four tonne crop as Mossie predicts. If I even get close, there'll be no stopping me. I've never had a four tonne crop and I'm not a complete slave to the truth.

Of course ALL is not well in Aberdeenshire.

We had a very cold spring, and there has been no rain to speak of for weeks. The silage is a minor disaster at about half its expected weight. (Not that we really expect to get the 'expected weight'.) The neeps are really suffering. Most people haven't even got enough to interest the pigeons. And everybody is short of grass.

My braes, which are supposed to feed the cows all summer, are like the semi-deserts I used to see in Kenya. When we took the calves in to worm them, they came in the sort of dust cloud which would have looked right in the Maasai Mara. It looked all wrong in Aberdeenshire.

I just had to get them off the braes so, as I write and pray for rain, I have forty cows, forty calves and a bull (which must count for at least two), on five acres down by the river. How long they can survive at sixteen to the acre, I don't know, but I await the phone calls. "Your cattle's oot on the road, Charlie Allan. Somebody micht be killed."

People who phone up in a lather like that, seem to think we don't care. They're right to some extent, of course. With hundreds of thousands of people starving to death throughout the world when the contents of our neighbours' dustbins could feed them, it is hard to get very excited about flutters in the hearts of the owners of the dustbins. But there is no way we farmers could ever be careless about our cattle getting on the road. Not unless we are very rich anyway. Have they not seen the price of fat stots?

And it's not just the grass that is suffering. There is a disaster brewing among the wheats on Scotland's cold shoulder. Many crops are showing acute water stress to the extent that the flag leaves are withering. That is serious, for the flag leaf is responsible for so much of the filling of the heads.

But my great-grandfather said of this place: "It'll neither droot nor droon." And that, once again, appears to be the case. So far at any rate, my wheat is not suffering. Indeed it has never looked better. But it is not headed yet, and we do need a good soaking, or the return of the drenching haar which has saved us so often. If we don't get either, my four tonne wheat crop is at risk, but I don't think anything can stop the barley.

Brace yourself banker!

I'm sorry I was overtaken by my uncle's funeral last week, and didn't keep my promise to tell you how the boys' practical joke on Mossie worked out.

You will recall that he went off for a week in Ibiza having sold an out-farm for more money than most of us can get into one dream. The plan was to ruin his holiday by flooding the Spanish newspapers with adverts saying that a well-known Scottish tycoon was in town looking for investment opportunities, and would welcome callers offering anything legal, and expressing an interest in several blocks of time-share.

There was a snag with this joke. There were no independent witnesses. We have to take Mossie's word for it.

He was just delighted.

"Oh aye," he told us with pride. "They'd heard about me oot there. What an offers I got! I could have had a share in a big block of flats full of pretty ladies who were awful short of clothes. The ladies seemed to want me to buy, for they kept waving to me. But I said no. Pigs work fine on flat decks, but that looked like trouble to me.

"There was a queue wantin to give me toasters, microwaves, and televisions, just to look at their time-shares. We couldna very well bring them all home but I got a buyer.

"And there was characters tryin to sell me new passports wi other folks' names on them. But I had a perfectly good passport. And what they thought I would be needing with dollars or Swiss francs, I don't know. They surely don't know the Salmon Inn only deals in sterling - or a brace of grouse, or a fresh-run fish."

Royal Highland Show 1994 preview

IN THE mid sixties, when the stock farmers of Scotland were beginning to turn their eyes to Europe in the hope that there would be some holy grail, or at least some manna there, there was a fashion for going to the Paris Show. Among the first to try it were two worthies from Aberdeenshire.

Stott and Willox who have sadly been gathered in now, were ubiquitous. They went to everything agricultural. There they took an interest, and made sure that the event was celebrated in a fitting manner. They taught me the intellectual, indeed mathematical, game of spunkie at the great spring show and sale of outwintered stores and stirks at Oban in 1973. So I owe them much.

It was entirely natural that Stott and Willox should be amongst the first to go to Paris for a look. I don't have a date, but it would have been in the late sixties when the Charolais were on their way and there was much interest, not just in seeing where they came from, but if there might be other cattle that could do well here, now that fears of them bringing foot and mouth disease had been overcome.

And Stott and Willox did indeed see a cattle breed of which they had not heard, and with which they were most impressed. The Chianina come from Italy, where they have been bred pure since the days when they used to pull ceremonial carts. They are even said to have been between the shafts when the Christians were being brought into the arena to feed the lions.

The main feature of these cattle is not their draft power but their height. Among cattle, they are always the first to know it's raining, for they are the tallest cattle in the world, and they were a source of great wonder to the two heroes who were used to the low-slung British beasts which still predominated here.

The warriors came home blowing that they'd seen a bull in Paris that was so tall, that it could fly cowpats clean over the taller of the two, Stott's bonnet, and that Willox, the shorter man, could walk under the brute's belly without bending down.

They may have been exaggerating, but not much. Chianinas arrived in this country in 1973, and were as tall as we could have hoped for, with mature animals going over six feet at the tail head. The fact that the tail head might be six inches above the small of their backs didn't deter the Yanks, who must have the biggest cattle in the world, even if they were the worst.

Soon, the lucky investors who had imported Chianinas were being besieged by stetsons with wallets as big as the mouths they sheltered. I had two Chianinas, and decided to ask plenty for the worst one. She had cost a staggering £2700, and I believe in a reasonable profit. I also believe in leaving a margin for negotiation, and asked £12,500. In negotiation you've got to start somewhere after all.

My price was accepted so readily that I had to admit to myself I hadn't asked enough.

I tell you all that, because it explains something of the excitement of going to an agricultural show, and the Highland is not an exception. Over the years, there have been some twenty new breeds introduced

to us at the Highland, and they are each said to have answered some farmers' prayers, though not usually with quite the munificence of the Chianinas. So we'll all be looking.

And I'll be looking at the machinery. I am a recent convert to machinery that works. I have spent much of my life farming with machinery that used to work, or might yet be made to work, or would have worked, had I but fed it sufficient oil and water. My association with Mossie has convinced me that that philosophy, and all the scarred knuckles and the bad language that go with it, is not the way forward. "Get the right stuff and keep it right, or you'll just get fed up."

He said that when I started keeping pigs. I took his advice and stopped feeding by cart tail-door, via old bath and augers, and got a fully automated system. Soon, I had a system in which the lorries arrived without me ordering. They filled my grain hopper, only calling to give me a delivery note, and every time a piggie took a mouthful, it was replaced while I slept.

I still got fed up of the pigs, of course, but that was because they were losing money. The system was a revolution and a revelation.

169

Farming can be fun, and there is no need for toiling and moiling any more.

That's why we trail round all those tired-looking trade stands. There might be something. Like the handle I got last year for £100 that stopped me bruising all my right flank, stretching round to shut off the sprayer.

One of the last jobs on the farm to become fun was the herding of cattle. I sometimes have nightmares about getting twenty Limousin heifers through a middle gate of a field. But, when I wake up, I realise that nowadays we have Honda the three wheeled dog, who can chase the cattle till they get tired.

Honda is now 17 years old, and we will be looking carefully for a replacement at the show.

So, it's not all beer and skittles with the boys.

But we'll likely end up as usual, speaking to our pals from home about what we'd be speaking to them about if we'd stayed at home.

We've managed to get a new hotel that hasn't heard of us, so here we go again. There's twelve in the team and there is a fight again to see who shares with Nicol from Keith.

But it's different from the fight last year. Then, no one wanted to share with him because of his snoring. This year, everybody wants to share with him, because it turned out that he was having such a jolly time last year, that he didn't need his bed till his room-mate was getting up.

" - forward, tho' I canna see, I guess an' fear."

170

Narrow escape for Red Rooster

I HAD a difficult job trying to bring the boys to order at the discussion group on Sunday. I don't know if it was the euphoria of having negotiated the Highland Show without serious mishap, but everybody seemed to be on a high horse.

Big Hamish was full of scorn about the modern trend towards providing counselling for everybody who has been involved in any distressing event. And what about the people who sued for the trauma caused by seeing spectacular disasters on the tele? Could they not just have put the tele off?

The thing that had really got him going was the reports that counselling was being provided for BBC staff to help them over the trauma of having filmed the D-Day commemoration. They might well have been upset by falling off their wallets stuffed with overtime payments, but there was agreement among the lads that they wouldn't have been much use fifty years ago.

Anyway, we have decided to put a stop to all this nonsense. We are going to support a test case in which Big Hamish sues Grampian region for the trauma he suffered when he looked over the dyke and saw a dead sheep - not just on the tele, mind - real, live, dead sheep.

And young Ochyoch is intrigued by all the extra information they are giving us. Not just where it will rain, but the latest bookie's odds against rain. Pollen counts and air quality seem to affect the English only, but it is interesting nevertheless. "What will they think of next?" he says. "What aboot the time taken to fry an egg on the bonnet of a Massey Ferguson 50B?"

And the Red Rooster, he's understandably full of his narrow escape from his fine new Charolais bull.

With the shortage of grass the Rooster, like me and half the countryside, has been feeding his cows on the grass. He had driven into the field, leaving the gate open on the grounds that the cows would prefer their cake to freedom.

The job done, the Rooster was making for the jeep when he felt a positive dunt in the small of his back. Don't believe anyone who tells you bulls don't go for red. This one did anyway, and he soon had our man down. He was settling into the kneeling-on-the-chest position by which many bulls have killed their handlers, when a remarkable happening saved the lad.

The cows, having finished their cake, proceeded to file out of the gate in search of pastures with some grass on them. The bull said that wouldn't do for a game of soldiers, and went after them. It was a very sore and very impressed Red Rooster that made it to the safety of his vehicle.

I know the feeling, for I once was saved by a bull's failure to keep his mind on the job. I was trying to halter Nester, my old Simmental bull, and I was trying to be a wee bit too clever.

I had the nose of the halter round the rim of a pail of cake. When Nester put his head in to eat, I popped the halter over his forehead - and I had him. Or more accurately, he had me. For he proceeded to rub me up against the byre wall. Luckily he decided that I was less interesting than the cake, and I was able to proceed, half tossed, half scrambling over his head and away. I was trembling.

So I understood why the Rooster was more impressed by his news than mine.

But my news is important. The whole of the Ythan Valley is threatened with being a 'Nitrogen Vulnerable Zone'. Apparently we are applying too much nitrogen to our fields, and it is running into the river and killing all the 'mud-dwelling Corophium'.

The trouble is that the boys have never appreciated the importance, or indeed the existence of, the mud-dwelling Corophia - so it's hard to get them excited about them.

But they should be excited about what it's going to mean to be in this Nitrogen Vulnerable Zone. The amount of nitrogen we use, whether in slurry, muck or bagged form, is to be strictly limited. We are not to use nitrogen (or muck or slurry) from September to February. We should not spray within ten metres of waterways.

But the whole thing is academic for the farmer of Little Ardo. As Mossie, yelping with delight, pointed out when he spotted it. "You're finished aa thegether. 'Do not apply nitrogen to steeply sloping fields.' Aa your parks are steeply sloping. You should've sellt the place. You're nae much o' a fairmer anyway."

Maybe I'll be as well out of it. All farmers are to keep records of all fertilisers and manures purchased *or produced on the farm*.

But it was hard to get the boys to be serious, though it is serious. There are no fewer than 68,000 hectares involved. I thought it would be more, seeing it includes Big Hamish, Crookie, the Red Rooster and Mossie.

It's not law yet, and I'm not selling yet. For example, how steep is a 'steeply sloping field'? And there is a very interesting phrase that occurs all over the place.

Nitrogen is to be banned 'unless there is a specific crop requirement'. What I think that means is you can put on the bagged stuff to establish the winter barley, but you may not splash on the slurry just to get rid of it.

For a grain grower, the nitrogen limits are higher than we are using at present. It is only those who dump slurry on the fields who are going to be severely restricted by this.

Nitrogen must not be put on flooded, waterlogged, frozen, or snow-covered ground. Well, no one would ever put bagged stuff on the first two, and it would be most unlikely to be put on the second two. In other words it is the intensive pig, dairy, and poultry boys who have a waste disposal problem who are going to suffer.

Little Ardo may be all right yet.

Too late to comfort the Gordons' piper

I DIDN'T get to the Show in the end. I was disappointed, but what can you do? There was just too much that came up.

For a start, the crisis with the grass not growing meant I was just too scared to go away from home.

My fences aren't good enough to keep well fed cattle in, and they are totally inadequate to the task of restraining them when they are hungry. So I just couldn't go away and leave the place without a toonkeeper. If I had, there is no doubt they'd have been all over the country.

We are really short of grass. Everybody is, but I'm in particular difficulty because, as you will remember, I've had to hold on to twenty stots for an extra two months to get the first subsidy. The Friday of the Show could have been sale day as I've now qualified for the sub but, with everybody away to the Show, it didn't seem worth exposing them. Even the auctioneers were pessimistic about the likely trade.

Then there was the combined 200 years celebration and wake for the Gordon Highlanders.

It was far too late for me to hold on to one of the stirrups of the Greys and charge into the French at Waterloo. I had no chance to comfort piper George Findlater after the Battle of Dargai. He'd continued to pipe the boys on with 'Cock o' the North' despite having both his legs shot from under him. I was too late even to give George Findlater VC half a crown when he was busking for a living on the streets of London after the war.

But, if Mr Major was to be flushing two hundred years of our history down the drain, I wanted at least to be able to say I'd been there at the two hundredth anniversary of a great institution. There'll be a Royal Highland Show next year.

According to Mossie, there were some important changes at this year's Show, mind you.

They have some new tables in the Members' bar, and there are several new staff at the

Herdsman's. Mossie found the staff changes particularly irksome (a sure sign of age). "These lads had nae idea what I was drinkin'," he complained.

I didn't see why that was such a terrible handicap. "Well, you try sayin 'mak mine a double gin and nae too much tonic and dinna tell the rest o' them it's a double,' after a whole day going round the stands."

Right enough, change can be upsetting.

And the show has had a profound effect on the boys. In fact, it has led to a C-change in their farming policy.

You see, this year the Show is quickly followed by the Crops Event. Now that promised to be something of a dis-

appointment.

It wasn't that the farms to be visited weren't of interest. Far from it. We, from the thin lands of Aberdeenshire, enjoy, in a masochistic sort of way, going down to the Howe of the Mearns and seeing how they are getting on where any fool who can scatter the good seed on the land is rewarded with three and a half tonnes of malting barley.

No, no. It's not that. The trouble with Laurencekirk is that it isn't far enough away. How can you possibly justify to the wife the cost and excess of taking a hotel for the night when you are only a big hour's drive away from home?

Mossie, who is married to a saint (would anyone less have

him?), was all for booking the whole team in for the night, but some of the other wives are of sterner stuff. They thought they were stretching a point letting their men stay the night at the Highland. After all, even the capital is only three hours away these days. Certainly there was no way we could get away with it when the Crops Event was no farther than Laurencekirk.

So we were beat again. But who would drive? Who would stay sober enough to remember the road north?

Of course, I wasn't there, but I'm told that there was a furious argument about who should drive. All the way down to the Highland they argued and bargued - and each gave reason and counter reason why someone else would be best to drive to the Crops Event.

I have to report that after the excesses of Edinburgh the argument rages on, but everyone has changed sides. The boys were so ill after Ingliston that they were all insisting that they would drive to the Crops Event. So heated did the argument become that, as I write, nearly everyone is taking their car to the Laurencekirk as protection against the demon drink.

There are two exceptions. "Sort yersels oot boys. Dae what ye like, but I'm nae drivin," is Mossie's response to it all. And, of course, I wasn't at Edinburgh and have not, therefore, learned its lessons.

But, for once, I am looking forward less to the social than to the farming aspects of the crops event.

I am a natural stockman. By that, I don't mean I'm good at it. I mean I have never seen much fun in watching crops grow. Crops have always been a necessary evil.

At Little Ardo, potatoes were grown to clean the ground and give the men something to do in winter. Turnips were grown for the cattle, and cereals have always been grown as much for the straw as for any grain we might sell.

But Mossie and Mr MacSharry have changed that. Having an expert for an honorary crops consultant has raised crop-walking from something I always intended to do, to something that is almost a pleasure.

Certainly, as the crop event looms, I find myself eager to see if there can really be crops that are looking better than mine. And even if the crops in the Mearns are better, my IACS forms will be just as good as theirs.

The nights are fairly drawing in.

Mossie gives the banker a terrible earful

ANOTHER EVENTFUL week has passed, with no loss of life by man nor beast.

The Royal Northern Crop Event was negotiated with honour. After the debacle of the Highland Show, the boys were full of good intentions when we set off and, really, their behaviour was exemplary.

Even Mossie was a bit off colour. Mind you, he was beginning to turn pink when I left to come home at five. He was in the Clydesdale Bank's tent - waggling the finger, and giving the bankers a terrible earful. There's nothing unusual about that, of course, it was what he was saying that really staggered the boys.

"And another thing, yer interest rates are jist a farce; far too LOW. All the time that I

177

was strugglin to service the overdraft I placed wi you when I was buyin farms and payin them up, you were chargin fifteen percent, or twenty percent. Now I've won through by sheer hard work and sellt Mossside - a sad day for the farmer when he has to sell his land - to try to get a few shillings in the bank for my old age. Bang! Doon comes the interest, and you're only givin me twa percent."

As he still has five farms, and has a good twenty years to go before he qualifies for the pension, we shouldn't feel too sorry for Mossie. I almost felt sorry for the bankers.

I also felt a bit sorry for the organisers of the crops event. They had done a superb job. Lots of trade stands, many with demonstration plots which had been many months in the preparation. There was a heap of fascinating, though unbuyable, machinery at work on the setaside. The star of the show, a pea viner - a combine which cuts, shells, washes, bags, prices and markets peas by remote control - cost £250,000 a piece or five for £1m.

It was a beautiful day. We had a steak from Carnegies, strawberries and cream from East Coast Viners, and drams from everyone - even the bank.

But the organisers had made one unfortunate mistake. The land on which most of the demonstration plots were grown had just come out of strawberries. Apparently, there is a chemical which they put on strawberries which is persistent, and can make growth difficult for what comes next.

When we saw the plots at first, we thought, "Us boys from the north can show these fat cats from the £3000 an acre land a thing or two when it comes to rape or cereals." They were not looking special at all. It is hopeless trying to demonstrate the effectiveness of four different fungicide treatments if the crop is so thin there is no fungal challenge to the untreated controls. Some plots had even been grubbed up, and substitute plants brought in in flower-pots.

It turns out that Strawberry Scramrot was to blame.

So does this mean strawberry growers are trapped in straws forever? Not really. There were two plots of winter oats which were quite impressive and, who knows, free of Scramrot it may be a real high-yielder.

The College had put a lot into a demonstration of crops we might grow on our set-aside. These were for the benefit of game, to give a bite for sheep in the back end, or to keep the land in production by growing non-food crops, like flax.

It was all very interesting, but we can't see how any of these crops are going to be an improvement on what we are doing at the moment. We take the set-aside money, bang on the systemic weed-killers, and clean the soil up for early-sown winter wheat. Ignoring the requirements of the wildlife, Mossie speaks for us all, whether we like it or not. "It's fantastic. This is the way forward. It's a giant step for mankind."

There's only the New Deer Cattle Show to go, and then we've a clear run through to Smithfield. Yes, we are getting there.

On the livestock side of the business, we made unsteady progress this week.

Having qualified for the first subsidy on my bullocks, having more or less understood the new system and got all twenty passports up to date with the numbers altered where necessary, I was all set. We've been so short of grass that they've been being fed, and so were easily brought in with the ever-willing help of Potions the chemist. Last spring's calves were looking well, and I was proud of my work as I waited for the float. It was due at a quarter to eight, giving an hour and a half for the run over to Inverurie.

The float arrived thirty-five minutes late with the excuse that he had taken three quarters of an hour to load his previous run.

"Pathetic!" I thought.

But mine wouldn't go in either. With half an hour to go, I sent him off with half a load. No! They hadn't carried pigs in the float the day before. In fact, they'd been away over to the west coast with a load of Boy Scouts.

Anyway, I missed my turn. I had visions of a repeat of the spring day when I had to sell my heifers last - to an empty ringside. In the event, there were so few cattle forward that they sold reasonably.

Four black and white steers made 130 pence a kilo, and the twelve averaged £97 above their weight in kilos. I had expected more earlier in the year, though not earlier in the day.

But what really shocked me was how heavy they were. That more than made up. I had been hoping for (but not expecting) £500 a head. The one steer which had gone fat weighed 635 kilos and grossed £718, while the stores averaged £577.

I don't know whether or not to be pleased that I have still got eight in the field.

The 1000 yards of misery had its many benefits

IT WAS a red letter day on Saturday. On that day, the Farmer laid his last load of ready-mix. Apart from the footpath that leads to the village, all the farm roads are now covered in cement, and there isn't a shed which has an earth floor.

There is a local verse of the old song which goes;

If I give you a braw farm toun,

Wi tarmac roadies all roon and roon,

Madam will ye walk

Madam will ye talk

Madam will ye walk and talk with me.

The Breadwinner has been walking and talking with the Farmer for 34 years, and taking the metalled roadies on trust. But now, at last, the job is done. It is even paid for.

And that's no mean feat, for I'm talking almost three-quarters of an acre of concrete here. I spent far more on cement for it than my father paid to buy the place. It was about fifty loads of ready-mix which now cost about £350 a load; a good £17,000 and the sweat of my brow. My father only paid £4200 for the title deeds, and he never even broke sweat.

When I see the grandchildren playing on their bikes round the steading on the clean cement, I think it was worth it. When I was their age, and arrived with my mother at Little Ardo to wait for my father to finish with Hitler and to come home to us, there was no cement.

The close was quite unmade. There were huge puddles when it rained, and great lakes of mud and strang in all but the driest weather. I remember the men sweeping and scraping the 'dubbs' (as it is called in our doric) into heaps at the sides, from which it soon oozed out again across everything.

One of the returned hero's first improvements was to cement the main close. Of course he was a gentleman farmer, so he only did it by proxy, but there was no ready-mix then. They laid out a smooth carpet of chukkies about an inch to an inch and a half in diameter, mixed up some very wet cement in an old tin bath, and then poured the contents over the stones.

It was so runny that it didn't need chapped with a stick to make it settle and gravity was all that was needed to level it. It seemed an unlikely method and yet, forty-eight years later, that stuff is holding up better than the first of my ready-mix - which was laid down twenty years ago.

A nice cement close was not unusual, but it was still a bit of a status symbol in Aberdeenshire fifty years ago. Ours improved things greatly. Now the biggest problem was the farm road.

To get to Little Ardo you had to negotiate seven hundred yards of council-owned road, and then three hundred and forty yards which we could only blame on ourselves. That made a thousand yards of misery, whose only benefit seemed to be that they put hawkers, commercial travellers, and Department of Agriculture inspectors off.

We did our best. Year after year we filled the potholes with gravel. Twice we re-metalled the whole lot with rotten rock from a nearby quarry. It never survived a winter. One good shower of rain seemed to be all that was needed for the pot-holes to get going again.

The Mackie's Milk lorry, which came each morning at eight, got the blame for churning up the roads.

The old man wanted the council to tar their seven hundred yards, but they kept refusing on the grounds that we were the only people using the road. However, my mother eventually wore them down. About 1960 she wrote to the Council pleading with them to mend the road. Her greatest fear, she said, was that when she died the hearse would be unable to get up to bear her body to the kirkyard.

That melted the hearts of the old Aberdeenshire County Council and they offered the old man a deal. If he paid one third, they would pay the rest and do the work. My father's share came to a mere £900.

But that still left our own three hundred and forty yards of lunar landscape for the hearse to negotiate. There was no way the council would pay two thirds of that, so out came the old tin bath again and two narrow strips of concrete were laid.

The idea was good. If the lorry driver was careful, he

could run with his wheels on the cement and that would save potholing the road. In fact, the strips seemed to develop continuous potholes along each side of their length. And they made the journey by car an absolute nightmare. The gauge of our cars was at least a foot too narrow to straddle the two strips. You could get one wheel on the flat, but the other was then in direct line to go crashing into every pothole.

It was only when the first Investment was getting married twelve years ago, that I finally got round to cementing the farm road properly. It would fairly have spoiled the wed-ding if some of the guests had crashed into a pothole and been drowned.

Anyway, it's all done now. The hearse has been and gone without a bump. Including nine hundred yards of public road which I tarred at my own expense, I've nearly a mile of roadies to offer the Breadwin-ner. I think I'll challenge her to come for a celebratory walk round them if it's a fine night. It is all so clean she'll be able to wear her high heels.

Some change! When she first saw Little Ardo, you'd have excused her if she hadn't been willing to chance it in her wellies.

Daughters will take over again

SUCCESSION IS much on my mind.

I suppose it was finishing the concreting of the farm roads that started it. Most of farming is a cycle; you sow and reap, and sow again. You put up a good fence; in five years it needs repaired, and in fifteen it needs replaced.

But improvements, like getting the cattle handling facilities up from a choke-rope in the byre and loading out of the neepshed door, to a proper race and crush and a loading bank, have a finality to them.

And so it was with the ready-mix. It was a poignant moment when the last driver swilled out and left the last mess at the roadside, and crashed for the final time over the verge of grass beside the byre.

It was always satisfying to see another bit tidied up, and it is sad to think that you will never again experience the pain in the lumbar region of the back that only chapping cement can give, that you will never again know the fury induced by a Wasting Asset tearing round a corner in the remains of a car and running two neat furrows through your wet cement.

The tenancy of the farm is a cycle. The young man takes over, usually when he is no longer young, and works his backside off until he drops. Then another middle-aged man, who has been waiting too long, at last gets his turn of the double bed in the front room up the old farmhouse stairs.

Little Ardo has been on that cycle for a hundred and fifty years though, in most cases it has passed not to sons but to daughters.

My great-great-grandfather William Yull, who put up the old barn in 1854, was succeeded by his son John. John had three sons but they didn't want the place. When they went off to the Empire, his daughter's husband, Maitland Mackie, took Little Ardo on as an outfarm. He sold it to his daughter, my mother, who by this time was Jean Allan, at the tail end of the war. I bought it from my parents in the late seventies.

183

Now that the roadies are metalled, and we've three new sheds up, I feel retirement coming up.

It isn't that there isn't anything left to do. The old steading which was done when my grandfather took the place before the first world war, is still done and must fall down soon. It needs clearing and a £60,000 multi-purpose shed put up. And yet I haven't the heart to salvage the slates and send for the digger. I fear a thunderbolt from Old William who built it, and my mother would certainly be furious.

So I am finished here. I should let the next generation in, and let them worry about finding the £60,000.

And I got another little reminder of the relevance of anno domine this week. On Saturday, I was at the New Deer cattle show, setting up the stall for the local heritage magazine. We've got a spanking new banner to fly over the entrance, and I had been fully employed for an hour or so rigging up a frame from which to fly it.

I was more or less finished, and quite pleased with myself, when the Red Rooster coasted up with his Range Rover and started telling me about how one post stuck in the ground with an old ruck centre tied to it, would never be strong enough.

When at last he did move off, I stepped backwards behind the Rangie for a better look at my work. I don't know what happened next, but I ended up on my back with a very heavy trailer bounding over my right foot.

I had not noticed that the Rangie had been pulling a rather snappy low cart. I don't think I'd have been so careless ten years ago.

So who is to be lumbered with the farm?

Clearly, the Wasting Asset is too busy developing the night-life of Aberdeen to take on the croft. His big brother, the Recovery Stock, is making such a good recovery, as a restauranteur, from his misspent youth, that there is no way he wants it.

So, once again, Little Ardo must pass down the female line. One of the Investments must take up my burden.

Here I must diverge slightly for I have not been entirely frank with you about Potions. He is a frustrated farmer and likes nothing better than to come down to Little Ardo to muck out a shed, or chase cattle on Honda, the three-wheeled dog.

It is an ideal situation for my farming. He's not that good but, then again, he's willing and he's easy paid. But Potions is not the soft mark you may be thinking. For he is married to the more mature of my Investments and he figures that the place may be his some day.

He's right too, for they are ideal successors to the little farm on the hill. It is she who has the qualification as a chemist, which leaves him free to come and play farmers. And when the bills start to land on their mat, the profits from the shop will help to secure the succession to yet another generation.

Mind you, I'm not going yet. Certainly not! Not when I've got Potions just where I want him, and the farm's paying for once. The crops are set for a bonanza, and even the calves are working.

I got the last lot away last Friday and, though the market was down, I seemed to prosper. The eight of them averaged 122 pence per kilo and were topped by a 504 kilo stot at 136 pence. The average price was £559 per head before the auctioneers started to feed.

Now, those would be disastrous prices for anyone who had bought his stores on the spring day for 150 pence per kilo. But when you bought their mothers for £56, and bred them yourself, I reckon it will do nicely, thankyou.

Falling victim to a wind-up

BY THE time you are reading this, I should be celebrating a record crop of winter barley, for the harvest starts on the 30th of July. I'll be very modest about it and hand over all credit to the fine summer, the great farm of Little Ardo, and to my crops consultant "without which none of this would have been possible."

I won't mean it, of course. In my heart I'll know that, once again, my diligence and skill have won a result despite the drought, the fact that I farm second-class land, and despite Mossie's advice.

How do I know the exact date of harvest?

It's quite easy really. The winter barley has been treated with Round-up.

I don't really like applying chemical sunshine, and in this year, which has been so sunny, it does seem a bit daft to start, but the fact is that one of the fields is a bit uneven and seems to have been sowed with an unmixed blend and, whereas the Pleasante was coming on fast, the Fighter looked to be a week behind.

And then, there is just enough couch in one of the parks to make Round-up seem worth while.

I'm not sure if the Guinness Book of Records would accept my measurements anyway, and I'm not quite sure what my record is. But I know I have had three tonnes twelve of barley and three tonnes sixteen of wheat. I also know that I shouldn't say this, it is just tempting fate, but I think the barley will be my heaviest cereal crop ever.

My only worry is that I may have to take a bit off my yields to make sure they are less than Mossie's. If I beat him - there'll be hell to pay, like last year when I had to make a quick recalculation of my winter rape yield.

It'll be a relief to get started, for this has been the silly season. There is nothing much to do in the run-up to harvest, and the boys have to fill their time somehow.

Someone always falls victim to a wind-up.

This year it was Mossie's son, Russell. He's a nice lad - quite unlike his father. He's quiet and unassuming.

It seems no time at all since Russell was sixteen and, therefore, old enough to drive a tractor on the road. He has been driving around in some style. He has cut quite a dash in the car park of the shooting club with his big Ford tractor.

But now he is seventeen, and on Thursday came that moment of truth for the farmer's son. Russell sat his driving test. You will believe that he is quite unlike his father when I tell you that he passed first time. That doesn't happen to many farmers' sons.

Russell could hardly wait to zoom into town and celebrate with his pals. It was all arranged and then "Bang!" What about insurance?

"A seventeen-year-old boy driving a Cosworth? Sorry sir, nothing doing. A Range Rover? Sorry. Not at any price."

Poor Russell was depressed. However, as he was leaving, tears not far away, to catch the bus for the town, his little sister whispered to him comfortingly. "It's OK Russell. I heard them talking. They're getting you your own car."

Oh the excitement! "What kind is it? When is it coming?"

"I don't know what kind it is, but it'll be here when you get home from the town."

Russell went off happily for his night out, and tried to keep quiet about his good fortune and the imminent arrival of his very own car.

When he arrived home at midnight, sure enough, there she was waiting for him beside the grain drier. In the half light he made out the balloons though he couldn't read the sign saying "Congratulations Russell. One careful owner (some time ago)."

And I can confirm that it was some time ago for, during the last eight years, that car has provided, in the close at Little Ardo, a nesting site for a pair of blackbirds in spring, and a bit of welcome cover in winter for a family of hedgehogs.

As Russell drew nearer to his car, he saw that it was a Ford estate car which was less sporty than he'd been hoping for. The flat tyre raised his suspicions, but it was the back door that doesn't close and the nettles growing out through the cracks that really gave the show away.

The poor boy clapped his hand to his forehead and exclaimed: "Wind-up!"

Now, although that old heap had been disgracing my farm for all those years and I was glad to be rid of such an eyesore, I had nothing to do with that. I'm not really into such adolescent games, especially when played by grown men. And just as domestic violence breeds domestic violence, I fear that Russell will now be confirmed as a winder-up. A wind-up has been sown and a whirlwind-up will be reaped, even unto a third generation.

I have observed a number of people being told of the great wind-up, and all have thought it funny up to the point where it begins to dawn on them that there is no happy ending. They all expected the final outcome to be that the young man awoke the next morning to find a shiny new car waiting impatiently for its young master to drive it away into the blue yonder.

There was no new car for Russell.

However his father's self-interest has provided a partial rescue. Mossie has been looking forward to being able to call on Russell to drive him home from the pub any time he was too tired. So he didn't take the lack of insurance cover lying down.

He has changed his insurance company, paid premiums increased by £900, and he's got cover for Russell.

"It's just a pound an acre on the overheads," he says, "Cheap at the price. Besides, wi the harvest coming up we'll be needing Russell's tractor."

Stookies make a brave sight

WELL, WE'VE got a start to the harvest. Three little fields of winter barley are safely cut and enough of it is away to the merchants for me to see that I have not got as much grain as I was expecting - but then long experience has taught me not to expect as much as that.

One of my clear memories of a childhood which is receding at an alarming rate, is of my father and his great grieve James Low, considering a crop of wheat they had just harvested. They stood at the top of the steep field which slopes south down to the river Ythan, my father smoking one of his Player's Please and Low scraping out his pipe and priming it with yet another fill of Bogie Roll.

They had achieved a record for the farm and, as far as they could recall, no one had harvested such a crop of wheat for miles around.

Normally, they wouldn't have known what the yield had been until the spring day when all the wheat had been thrashed out of the stacks in which they were stored all winter. But this time the stuff had been so dry that they had thrashed it out of the stooks. That saved an amount of work that is almost unthinkable today. And they had got an immediate result.

It was easy. They just had to count the bags, multiply by two and a quarter and divide by the acres. Fifty-two hundredweights to the acre! It was a wonder. James Presly, whose farm glowers at Little Ardo across the valley, wouldn't be able to come down to the village for a week for fear of bumping into us.

I remember James Low boasting to me many years later that the stooks in that park were so tightly packed that they had to reverse the tractor in to get the first load. The stookies made a brave sight. I remember them well, but they were not as close as all that. It was only a six-acre park but it was a record in its day. In the twenty or so years that the two farmed on, they never beat that yield, though many others round about them did.

189

So you can see why I am so desperate to get to four tonnes. Oh, I know four tonnes is just a little short of eighty hundredweights, being not at all the same as four tons. But I think of the wonder the old men will show when I see them hereafter and tell them that I have grown four tonnes of barley in the Home field. They'll never know that a tonne isn't as big as a ton used to be.

As a matter of fact, impressing the old men about my farming achievements may not be easy. I know what the old grieve will say for a start. It will be just like the time I told him that grass in Ayrshire had made fifteen pounds an acre. He looked at me with a virulent mixture of pity and contempt and said that if I believed that, I'd believe anything.

Yes, I may need proof and it could be tricky sneaking that through purgatory.

But I run ahead of myself. First I must harvest the four tonne crop.

It is not easy to estimate a crop until it is in the bank. When it is growing it looks at its best. It usually comes down a hundredweight or two once it is cut. Combine tankfuls are a very unreliable guide to yield but they are a bit better than the naked eye, especially when it is a proud farmer's eye looking at a standing crop.

Two of my fields, of Pleasante the six-rowed winter barley, have looked much my best ever, raising the dreams of four tonnes once again - maybe four and a half? By the time we were counting the tankfuls it was down to just over the four. Now we have enough away to the grain merchants to see that the Glebe is going to yield around three tonnes fifteen. And the Home field was a bit better than that, and I can dream on.

So I've got more than seventy-five hundredweights and the old men would be astonished.

But I am not astonished that they grew such small crops. There is so much more which we do nowadays to make the stuff yield. We have perhaps five sprays and three applications of fertiliser. We keep every fungus known to man off them, make sure the little plants have no competition from weeds, and we spray them into thinking they are fully grown when they are only small so that they put the rest of their energy into making grains.

Now, when old Jimmy taught me how to grow barley he told me about ploughing it properly, and making a good seed bed. He showed me how to put the seed in to the correct

depth, and how to harrow and roll.

All of that advice was right, but his last words were quite wrong, "Then shut the gate. Ye willna need it till hairst time."

Of course, with his record winter wheat crop, he did need the gate in the spring time to put on the two hundredweight of nitro-chalk, but otherwise the wheat had to grow itself.

And, when you look at the old men's record in that light, it really was quite a feat. For all my seventy-five hundredweights of barley I wouldn't like to try to grow fifty-two hundredweights of wheat with no more stimulus than two bags of 'nitre' - and no more protection than that provided by irregular attendance at church.

Young Mains is making a splendid job of the combining. I have enjoyed the high yields but I have also enjoyed Young Mains, who is unusual in that he has a regard for the past. There is something additionally droll about a man of his years telling the stories which are normally told by grey beards.

191

Red Rooster has an ocean of barley

THE FARMER can die happy. We have four tonnes and forty four kilos to the acre in the Home field.

I keep waiting for a rumble of distant thunder to let me know that the old man has recognised my achievement. None has come so far, so I may indeed have to die to realise my triumph.

Of course, as my father used to say, "The bite's nae yours till it's in yer mou". Many disasters are yet possible before we get winter, but things are going well with the harvest.

What a contrast with last year. Then, we had 21 hundredweights less to the acre and that had to be put through the wringer to get the water out before the dryer would take it. The drying charges will be low this year, though I did panic a bit and cut the barley maybe a day or even two, too early. We had one sample as high as 21 percent but we had another as low as 16.

Young Mains has made a grand job of the combining, though that's no more than you would expect with the weather so fair. At times the stour was flying out of the old John Deere as though she was on fire. And if the conditions were a contrast to last year, they were also, as Mains pointed out, a big contrast to 1933, the very dry year known as 'The Year of the Short Corn'.

In that year my mother's cousin, Bruce Mackie, had his honeymoon timed so that he would be home in time for harvest. In the event, they arrived back at Rhynie just as the last load was entering the cornyard. He had made it in time to see the winter sheaf put in place.

But I digress from my digression. Young Mains is unusual for a man of his years in that he has an interest in the past, and in the wisdom of old men. He also has a nice line in exaggeration - something else we share in common.

I took him a beer in the middle of the afternoon. The excuse was to wash away the dust of the day, but the reason was to get him to stop the combine so that we could have a 'heavying' session about what a grand crop we had, and what a great job we were making. It was then that the old man's talk issued from the young man's lips.

"What a bout of straw, Charlie. Some contrast to the year o' the short corn. They had to straw their boots across that year because the corn wasna long enough to reach the toes."

Of course, the trouble with having a good crop in a good year is that everybody else is liable to have a good crop too. And the fact that I was one of the first to cut hereabouts meant that my crop was more or less bound to be beaten. The lighter crops normally ripen first.

In fact, I was just taking a break from phoning up every-body to tell them about the Home field when I got a call from Mossie. "Do ye want to see a right crop of barley? We're cuttin the best crop you've ever seen for the Red Rooster. The berries are that big we've had to throw out every second wire from the concave just to let them through. What a crop!"

Generous of spirit though I undoubtedly am, this was not altogether good news for me. But, if you are to have any friends, you have to show a bit of enthusiasm for their successes. That is especially true if you want them to show any enthusiasm for your own. Over I went.

And there they were, the Red Rooster and Mossie in their monster combines, crawling up and down the most exquisite

crop of Manitou, six-rowed barley, with the clouds of dust billowing round them.

Somehow they reminded me of two pirate captains of old on the bridges of their galleons. With greedy eyes they gloated down on the golden booty. My Home field is 15 acres but this was a prairie - nay, an ocean.

Onward and onward ploughed the galleons, back and forth across the undulating brine. The stour when it caught the sun was like a foaming spray, and the billows of stour were thrown out by the salvoes of the cannon as another golden tankful was pillaged. And there on the bridge - the two captains, eye patches, headkerchiefs and cutlasses. A passing pigeon could even have been a parrot.

I climbed onto the bridge to pay my respects to Captain Rooster. "Great crop. How much do you think you've got?" "Well, you know me Charlie. I dinna like to blaw till it's all dried and away to the mill, so I'm nae sayin - but it could be four and a quarter - at least."

There's always something in farming to bring you down, even if it's only your friends. On top of that, we've no grass for the cattle, a cow has died of mastitis, and the wheat is burning - and will be among the first in the district to be ready.

In spite of those little difficulties, life seems good just now on top of the little hill that overlooks the village of Methlick. And my feelings of the goodness of it all climaxed when Mains finished cutting the Home field. He would leave the combine and I would give the combine driver a run home. It seemed only right that I should make an exception and take him home in the Jaguar. As I explained at the time, "It wouldna do for lads that have just cut a four tonne crop to be seen in an old diesel Cavalier."

Cornyard makes Mossie whoop with delight

WHAT A week I've had. Talk about progress. Here we are in the middle of August and we've got a quarter of next spring's work done already.

The three fields which averaged three tonnes thirteen of winter barley are back into crop already. They are desperately trying to find enough moisture to start the germination of the rape crop of 1995.

They are having a struggle though. It has never been so dry in anyone's memory. Oddly enough, the ground water situation was much worse in 1989, but the topsoil is much drier this year. The plough was followed by clouds of dust, as was the one-pass which sowed our seeds. In a frantic effort to conserve any water there might be in the soil, the plough, the one-pass, and the heavy roller worked close together. The three clouds of dust moved up and down the fields with hardly a break.

Of course, the seeds will be alright as long as it stays dry.

There is no way they can germinate when it is like this. They could last for years, decades maybe. The trouble may come when the rain does come. If we get less than half an inch of rain, the seeds may germinate, send roots down into the dust, and shrivel and die.

But let us not look on the downside, for there is much about which to be optimistic - especially if you are Mossie.

He's just rouped the straw he grew on the farm he sold this summer, and the roup was something else. I stopped counting when the fifty-fifth car came into the park. I have never seen a roup of straw attract more than a dozen cars.

And when the sale got going, all previous records were annihilated. Last year, some were sold for £9 but that figure was soon passed. Indeed, the first lot was sold for no fewer than £11.40 a bale.

And stranger still, the successful (if that is the word) bidder was none other than

Potions the chemist. Now, I know that he has strawberries, and that his daughters have always fancied guinea pigs, but what on earth is he to do with fifty-six big bales of straw? That's a good ten tonnes unless you believe that Mossie would do anything so underhand as to make the bales light in order to have all the more to multiply by the winning bids.

It turns out that Potions had a buyer, and I was very glad to find that that buyer wasn't me.

I was even gladder that I didn't get landed with the rape straw. Our man was bid no less than £9.50 per acre for his rape straw, and it hasn't even been combined yet.

It is a few short years since Mossie was harvesting that straw with a matchbox, and here he was getting £8,000 for the by-product of a farm which was no longer his.

Frankly, it makes me and many others sick.

Mind you, there is no good reason, apart from jealousy, why we should be so upset. I don't need to buy any straw and those huge prices mean that I could make similar money if only I had the courage to sell the bovine bank unbalancers.

But I won't, so I too have been busy with the straw.

I've wrapped a hundred bales and treated them with ammonia to help feed the cattle. Now, the College tell us that wheat straw is better for feeding, and the cows tell us the same thing. Indeed we intend

to take them through the winter on treated wheat straw.

But this lot isn't for winter feed. This hundred bales of treated barley straw is to get mine through the rest of the summer. They would get more sustenance from a tarmac road than they're getting from the grass just now, so dry is the North-east.

One of the problems with treating all this straw is finding the room to store it. The old corn yard is nowhere near big enough, and we need the Dutch barns for grain stores before they can be filled with straw.

But we've solved that one in the most agreeable way imaginable. The government is going to pay me to have a spanking big cornyard. It is another aspect of the blessing of set-aside. Mossie is still collecting for the statue to MacSharry. I must remember to increase my donation. From now on, we just have to set aside one hectare of one of the home fields each year, and there we have a cornyard of wondrous size, and carrying a subsidy of £292 per annum. And who knows? That may rise.

This year's cornyard has the added benefit of cutting off the gushet in the Home field. She's sown in winter rape, and there will be no annoying little short passes with the sprayer this year.

And already my cornyard has given the greatest pleasure to Mossie. He whooped with delight when he saw it. "You've had it boy. You'll lose aa your subsidies if you put that in for set-aside. Do you nae read the bookie? Set-aside must be at least twenty metres wide, and I canna see the thin end o' yer gushet passin for twenty metres. They have a little wee mannie workin in the Department. You could ask for him. Maybe he would mak it twenty paces - but nae twenty metres." And he proceeded to pace the narrow end of the gushet with exaggerated little steps, and unconcealable delight.

I should just have sulked, but stupidly I tried to hit back.

"Well, you're in for it tae," I said pathetically. "Wait till the tax mannie gets onto your Pick-Your-Own sunflowers, boy. You'll have some bill, I can tell ye."

"Well Charlie, you're richt aboot one thing, at last. But I've tried farmin withoot the tax man, and I can tell you - that's nae a success."

Nostalgic link with mill dam

THE BOYS are scandalised. They just can't understand me. They think I have lost the wee bit sense I had.

You see, right in the middle of harvest, I have just spent a very small fortune - and quite a bit of this week - cleaning out an old mill dam. Worse than that, it is not an elaborate ruse to get grant money out of the EC, or out of the Society for the Preservation of Rural Scotland; I am paying for it all myself. And even more worse, the dam is not on Little Ardo, but on Penny Washer's farm.

In the days when Newseat of Ardo stood on its own as a sixty-acre mixed arable farm, the function of the mill dam was to drive the thrashing mill. When he was ready for a thrash, old Newseat would open the sluice at the dam, and enough water would come tumbling down the lade to turn the big water wheel that powered the mill.

It was quite a feat of engineering, for there was not much fall in the ground, and there was no more than a good trickle of water filling the dam between thrashes.

Of course, the dams and the waterwheels mostly went out of business between the wars, when the mills came to be powered by tractors. By the time I was a boy, the dam here at Little Ardo had been built over, and my grandfather's new barn had started to subside into it.

Newseat's dam, on the other hand, had just started to decay gently. It had started to silt up, and weeds were encroaching from one side. But it was still a magical place when I was boy.

There were often a few mallard ducks swimming there, and each year, among the weeds, I used to search out the water-hen's nest. I wish I could remember how many eggs she had, but I'd be guessing. All I can remember is that it seemed to be a large number like ten.

There were fish in Newseat's dam. They were not huge, even in the memory faded by fifty years, but they were lively brown trout which must have made their way up to the dam some very wet spring. Certainly, there were many times when there would not have been enough water in the little stream to wet their backs. In summer nights they were a joy - leaping clear of the water to take the flies. They seemed particularly active in that, and I always presumed that, with so little water flowing into the dam, they had to rely heavily on what they could pluck out of the air.

There were puddocks galore in the dam, and many's the mess of spawn I carted home as a child - and killed by ignorance and neglect. That was most likely a worse fate than growing to a size that would tempt the graggy heron, who reversed the feeding role of the fish, plucking his food from the water.

But the Newseat dam continued to silt up. At last, the water found a way of cheating the dam altogether. The lade leaves the dam near where the little stream enters it. The old sluice decayed and, of course, the water took the shortest route to the sea and went straight out down the lade.

The dam dried up and became no more than an untidy corner of Newseat's top field, the one that marches with Little Ardo. The heron and the puddocks died out or moved on.

But now Penny Washer, the white settler, has put in a fancy new sluice. If that is shut the old dam could be filled if only we could get the sludge out. And we did just that last week.

You'll remember Mr Twenty-percent the digger salesman who, when he sells a new digger for £30,000 takes your old machine back and makes 20 percent on selling that, which means he has an older machine to sell, and so on until he has pocketed the whole £30,000? Well, he's got a JCB 814-Super crawler-digger and it was stuck at £17,000, so I was able to do a deal, at a pint of beer less than £400, to clean out the old dam.

What robbery! That machine shifted the sludge faster than I would have believed. In four hours she was clean to a depth of five feet and my field, on the north side of the dam, had a huge new feature - the biggest pile of silt and sludge you'll see.

Standing in Newseat's dam while the water trickled in, filling the tooth marks left by the monster digger, I marvelled at progress. She had cost a hundred pounds an hour, and yet she was worth it. I imagined the gallant men in the last century who had dug this great hole by pick and spade, and had loaded the lot by shovel. And remember, the digger only had to shift silt whereas the old men had had stones, rock, and the hard pan to deal with.

But the boys are still puzzled. Why would I clean out Penny Washer's dam?

Crookie thinks he knows. All that sludge is what has run off the fields in the last hundred years. "That stuff may be sludge to you but its practically solid 20.10.10. It's cheap manure he's after."

And the Red Rooster thinks

I'm after a reservoir to fill my sprayer at, though Mossie says I can forget that. A dam is hopeless as you get silt off the bottom which chokes the filters.

Penny Washer thinks I have cleaned out his dam for some sly reason but, if he knows what it is, he's not saying.

They're all wrong. It is pure nostalgia. And when the water-hen nests there next year, I'll be able to see her and find her nest, whoever owns the dam.

200

God is a good cattleman in summer

I'VE TAKEN a fair bit of stick this week over my scheme to dredge Penny Washer's mill dam so that I can enjoy once more the wildlife that nested, flew and swam there when I was a boy.

The main plank has been that anybody who can hire a digger for £100 an hour (even for four hours) to clean out somebody else's dam in the middle of harvest, must have very little to do. I'm afraid that that is true.

The middle of harvest it is, and worse than that, we are also right in the middle of what used to be the spring work. We have harvested the winter rape and the winter barley, and sown all the cleared parks with more winter rape. And yet there is little to do, as we wait for the wheat to ripen.

That is what mechanisation has done to life on this small farm. At this time, my father used to take on an extra man, two if you counted me, which gave a total force of eight, or nine if you counted him. But now there is only me and contractors.

It is true that I could be busier if I did away with the contractors and did all the heavy work myself, but I wouldn't be able to do that for long. I'd very soon be broke. The heavy machinery costs these days mean that contractors provide the only way. They charge me something like £10,000 a year, and that saves me buying maybe a quarter of a million pounds worth of gear - and as we say in our discussion group, "That jist willna coont."

So Davie comes with his two five-furrow ploughs and tractors at £40,000 a piece, and his tractor and one-pass at another £50,000 and sows my crop. Mains comes with his £80,000 combine and cuts it, and Davie sends £100,000 worth more of tractors and balers over to bale it. All the Farmer has to do is cart off the grain and the odd stone with his 1946 Bert Grant cart (£164), take off the bales with his new transporter which takes four at a time (£600), stack them with the digger (£2,300), spray for weeds, pests and moulds (£1500) and worry. I have missed out my new and shiny tractor from Poland, but that is quite fair as I keep it in the shed - unless I am going anywhere where I might be seen. All of those jobs can be done with the old International (£1800 in 1984).

I do, of course, have a hundred head of cattle to add to the worry of the job, but the fact is that, even in a dry year like this, God is a pretty good cattleman all summer. It is only in crises and in winter that the cattle are much work for the Farmer.

But all that didn't stop the boys taking the Micky out of my harvest project - especially when the mill dam refused to fill up. "What a duck shootin you're goin to have there Charlie. Are ye goin to stock it wi pike for a bit o' sport? Is it boatie rides that you're goin to start on the auld mill dam?"

At first I thought the problem was that it was a very large dam and, due to the drought, there was no more than the fill of a half inch pipe running in. But it soon became clear that even the trickle was escaping. After many years of running down the lade to where the thrashing mill had been, the water was reluctant to go into any mere dam. It had found its own way back in to the lade, despite Penny Washer's smart new sluice being shut.

Anyway, by Sunday I had cracked that, and the water stopped going down the lade, so I presumed the dam must be filling, though there was little immediate evidence. I was explaining all that to the boys at the discussion group when the Red Rooster came in. I could see he was impressed.

"What a success that duck pond o' yours is Charlie. It's jist full o' ducks aaready."

"How many?" I stammered, unused to such success, and for want of anything else to say.

"Well there was that many I couldna coont them," said the Rooster, "and I saw them first so if anybody gets to the shoot, I've to get."

Well that shut them up though, I suppose, thinking back, I should have noticed the odd smile and wink that went on among my fellow members of the discussion group.

As early as might be without attracting suspicion or detracting from my cool exterior, I stole off home via the

dam. Would the ducks still be there?

With the nights drawing in, I wasn't sure if I'd be able to see much as I crept up to the edge of the reeds and peered in. And there were ducks all right. I could see why the Rooster had had difficulty counting them - though I wasn't long in guessing that there would be exactly 200 ducks on Penny Washer's pond.

They didn't look quite right somehow, even in the fading light and to my fading eyes. But when one swam closely past I did see, quite distinctly, a number on its back.

Each year there is a race between the two bridges at Methlick on the river Ythan. You pay a pound to buy your plastic duck, and the winner gets £50 - with the other £150 going to 'the funds.' The boys, who would still be boys despite all the physical impediments they have accumulated over many years, had borrowed the whole 200 and floated them in the old mill dam.

I hope the 'funds' benefited substantially.

They looked rather jolly but, as the water level rises, I do fear the plastic flotilla may scare off the mallard who should arrive any day.

'Shedding' my white elephant

IN MY diary in 1978, I wrote with such pride about my new shed. It was more than a shed. It was a factory. Instead of chasing feeding cattle all over Aberdeenshire all summer, and feeding them silage all winter, I would have a barley-beef factory. This would pour out a steady stream of fat cattle, and into the bank would pour a steady stream of money. Despite the initial expense, and the considerable debt already hanging over my enterprise at Little Ardo, all would soon be flowing with milk and money.

The idea seemed good enough. An English supermarket chain was willing to pay top market prices for barley-fed entire bulls. Those could be had cheap from the local dairies, or brought up from the south for even less. Friesian bulls were cheap for a good reason - they're not very good. And feeding them nothing but barley made them even worse, but why should we worry if the thing paid? I certainly didn't worry in those days - I even found myself chairman of the co-op that organised the production of several hundred of the brutes a week - though I now think that producing beef fed on barley, and killed before they have had two summers on the grass, is just what the beef industry does not need.

Anyway, it seemed that, in Mossie's ridiculous phrase, 'This was the way forward.' Indeed, it seemed, 'a giant step for mankind.'

The plan was that all the barley would go into a grain tower at harvest. Next to the store would be a bruiser-house, and from there the beasts' diet would proceed by a series of augers, elevators, and conveyers, straight into the hoppers in my brand-new slatted shed.

With the slats, there would be no mucking. I would just attach a hose to the great tanks, suck the slurry into the sludge cart the Breadwinner gave me for my birthday, and spray the fields with this excellent liquid fertiliser.

The whole thing was to be so automated that I would feed my 132 bulls from a switch at my bedside. Even that plan didn't last. The aim was to achieve the same results as the system which we now use in the piggery, whereby every time a pig takes a bite, the machinery all goes on and the bite is replaced without all the effort of putting on the switch at your bedside.

Now, you may well have spotted flaws in this plan. You may even have noticed a certain irony in the way I have been writing. Nevertheless, the Farmer was a proud man when he put the first of the bulls onto the slats. It was the first shed to be built on Little Ardo since my grandfather's in 1936. In the building stakes, I had already beaten my father - and I'd only just got the reins.

The bulls weren't that impressed though. Where was the straw? Surely there would be more than barley to eat? Was there to be nothing to make a cudd of? And how were they supposed to get down to the water they could see glinting far below the slats?

Right enough, they had far too little to do. After a few minutes they had filled their bellies with barley - and all that remained to do was to try the catches with their tongues. In no time, the Farmer was back to chasing bulls round the countryside. We eventually got spring clips to keep the bolts shot, but it took us a long time to beat them.

And the slats really didn't seem to agree with the bulls. Why should it? A life of eating and sleeping on concrete certainly doesn't sound ideal. The biggest hazard seemed to be that they tramped on one another's tails. Ten percent of the tails went septic, and often they had to be put down. As the whole harvest went into the sealed grain tower unweighed, we really didn't know how much they were eating. So it took a financial crisis to persuade me that the bulls weren't paying.

And my fancy electronic feeding system never worked. There were just too many parts to go wrong - and they did.

All in all, my factory was just a white elephant, which would never have been put up had it not been for the grants that were then available under the infamous Farm and Horticultural Development Scheme.

The grain tower has been empty for years now. The elevator, which cost a fortune all those years ago, and which never turned a wheel, is now a nesting site for an impressive colony of pigeons. And the old steel baths which we decided to use when the money for hoppers ran out, are all in the

rubbish dump, except for the one we sold to the Irish antiques shark.

The shed has been converted into winter quarters for my hill cows. From a loss-making activity it has been converted to one which loses much less intensively. One lot of slats have been done away with, so that they have a nice strawed bit for lying on and they get up on the slats at the other side of the pass to feed and, hopefully, to dung.

It is nearer to being a sensible shed now, and it is certainly more cattle-friendly. But great snags remain, the worst of which is that the slats con-gealed two winters ago and I had to spend £200 getting Big Hamish to come with his fancy digger and clean it out.

Now the same thing has happened again and I'm losing patience. Big Hamish may be back again, but this time it'll be to remove the centre pass, and make the whole thing into an old-fashioned court.

If I hear a snigger from the rigging when we're doing that, I'll know it is my father. He warned me well that, in a changing world, buildings should be flexible. He was right. Of my fancy new factory, all that will remain is the roof and three walls.

Necessity of giving straw a try

THIS IS the way forward. I'm not sure that I like it, but it is impressive. Another giant step has been taken by mankind. Harvests will soon be over before they are started.

The latest breakthrough is the treatment of straw with ammonia to make it more digestible and palatable for the cows. We've been forced into it by the failure of the summer rains, which have made so many of our recent harvests a misery.

This year there was hardly a drop between April and September, so it was a difficult enough job keeping the cows fed - let alone producing a surplus for making silage. So we are treating most of the cereal straw.

The salesman tells me that with a bit of concentrate, it will do just as well as silage. Of course, he is selling, so he may not be the most impartial of judges, but necessity is the mother of giving it a try this year. Buying silage just isn't an alternative as no one has any to sell.

And what a difference it makes to the already breakneck pace of harvest. Take the case of the Barn park, which went through its harvest metamorphosis this week.

On Tuesday morning, the water we had longed for all summer was shrouding a scene which could hardly have looked less like harvest, and certainly foreboded not the transformation that was about to hit the field in which William Yull decided to build his barn in 1854.

By midday it had cleared up, and by half past three I had Mains and his combine in the field and ready to go. The wind was drying it - but slowly. Mains couldn't see what all the hurry was, especially as we had still been cutting in the first week of November last year. Still, there was twenty pounds an acre to be made so off he set.

Luckily, I haven't got the returns yet so I can't tell you how wet it was, but by the time we were on to our third load it was reasonable - maybe twenty-five percent. By half past six we were within sight of finishing the park and I telephoned Davie, the contractor of few words, to come and bale it.

And that is the breakthrough. Normally, if you are conserving straw for fodder, you have to wait a few days for the sap to dry out - and in bad years like last year, that may never happen. Even if you harvest straw in the English manner, with a box of matches, you have to wait for it to dry in Aberdeenshire. But with straw treatment, it is best baled hard behind the combine.

I called Davie at 6.30 and the man of few words left with two balers at 7.00. By 8.10 he had driven five miles to Little Ardo and had baled the fourteen acre field. Those two monsters tore up and down in the second top of eight gears and, with the combine, did the job which consumed man-weeks when I was a boy.

It seems no time since we started by cutting once round the field with a scythe to let the binders in. That was done when the corn was still green, so it could be a fortnight later before the binder started. Then we stooked it into eights. There it stood for another week or so to ripen and dry further. Winds would come and knock the stooks down, and we'd have to set them up again. In desperation we would knock them down ourselves and turn the wet bottoms of the sheaves up to the wind to dry and then, lest rain come, we'd re-stook all those which we couldn't get home.

Large parts of the British Empire were founded on Aberdonians' desperation to escape from setting up stooks.

After that, the sheaves had to be built onto carts - and built from there onto rucks, and then in winter we'd fork the rucks back onto carts again, and from there onto the thrashing mill which stood timeless in the barn.

But in under four hours we had achieved all that on Tuesday. And the story gets better. By lunchtime on Wednesday, we had the Barn park cleared and Davie was back, not just with his wrapper but with two ploughs and a one-pass. In two days, we went from a standing crop of wheat to a crop of next year's winter barley safely into a warm bed.

There was one year in the 1950s when we managed the harvest, which at that time was all spring barley, in three weeks of continuous toil. Usually, it took much longer, and involved much more toil. But now there is no toil. Harvest proceeds in a series of short bursts, and each is over before you know it. In another big week, we'll have all the spring work done as well. What a time we'll have then.

So, have we made it? Is this indeed the way forward? Can there be any more progress to come? The only thing I can think of is that we might sow several years' crops at once. Each could be chemically treated so that they didn't germinate until the year we wanted them.

Of course, Mossie has had a breakthrough all of his own. The boys can't see that it is such a revolution, but the lad is impressed. He has got the wife into harness.

When the hash was on at Moss-side, Mrs Moss would drive the tractor to bring home the grain from the combine. As Mossie advanced up the field, his heart was warmed by the sight of his lass spinning towards him in the massive Ford.

In a flash she was past, but Mossie has been very nice about it. He has refused to make fun of her for failing to notice that unloading on the move works best if both combine and tractor are facing the same way.

"No, no." he says. "It was very good. It jist didna give me much time to unload, even wi' the seventeen-tonne cart."

Bare footed into the land of the free

IT WAS around 1980 when the Farmer decided on a holiday to the United States of America. He had just had a very good sale of pure Simmental Cattle at Edinburgh's Gorgie market at the time of the Royal Highland Show, so there would be plenty of money to buy the booze. With him were the Breadwinner who was well ready for a holiday from teaching, the younger Investment, who even in her early teens was adding value by the day, and the Wasting Asset who, though he was inattentive at school, had not yet got seriously into wasting.

The plan was to see Washington and New York, and then visit a farmer friend in Kansas City, Missouri. That was all done. But the holiday got off to a humiliating start.

There we were, at Kennedy Airport. We stood, metaphorically at least, where the world's poor and the world's persecuted had stood, waiting for the nod to enter the land which promised them so much. It never occurred to the Farmer that the immigration man would not be eager for him to pass into the Land of the Free - after all, he had just had a successful sale at the Highland. But the Hope of the Brave was not to be gratified at once.

"I see you're a farmer, sir."

"Oh yes. Little Ardo, you know. Fine place. Two hundred and fifty acres with three hundred yards of the river Ythan."

The customs man didn't seem to be impressed with the details of my prairie.

"And have you been on the farm recently?"

"Well, not for a day or two. You see I've been down at the Highland for a few days. I sold my herd of Simmental cattle. I got nearly fifty thousand pounds for them - that's about eighty thousand dollars to you." said I helpfully.

The customs man still didn't seem that impressed. "Can I see your shoes sir?" I began to get just an inkling of the terror the poor Jewish immigrant might have suffered between the wars.

Off came the shoes.

They were a rather nice pair of brown brogues with what used to be called brothel-creeper soles - great thick things. And it was those soles which were to be the source of my humiliation. They had a deep ribbing designed to give the wearer a firm grip of Scotland.

Unfortunately, they had done that rather too well and, when the customs man turned the shoes upside down, he could greenish sawdust which I recognised from the Gorgie market.

"I'm sorry sir, but you can't come in here with those." But I had no other shoes and I wasn't going to enter the Land of the Free in bare feet. I thought the Breadwinner, and her two children were smirking as they passed through and I rummaged in my case for a toothbrush to take to the toilet to manicure my offensive shoes.

That done, they let me in.

see that the ribs were quite full of the evidence of my movements over the previous few days. You could see the dark soil of Little Ardo, and the highly organic compound you get round the cattle rings at the Highland. There was also some

But I have been nervous of customs men ever since.

I have told you that story because it was a low point in my farming career. For some reason, it is much easier to write about your misfortunes. It seems so boring when all is

211

going right.

And that is the situation on top of the hill. I don't have exact figures yet, but the harvest is very good and very easy. The rains have come at last, so there is enough for the cattle to eat for the first time this summer. The season is so early that I am taking the opportunity to get out of spring rape and winter wheat altogether, so that next year's harvest will be finished in August.

I have eighty-five acres of oilseeds in the ground and looking really well, and fifty acres of winter barley which is at least in the ground. All should be in during September and, as long as it is, all should be well next August. By the end of the week I'll have all the spring work for 1995 done.

We have had to push on a bit to get this far thus soon. It really shouldn't have been necessary to take the wheat at an average of 24 percent in so dry a year, but it seems worth it to get out of those late crops for good.

The last load of wheat, in particular, should have had a bit longer but, even when the dew is down, it is hard to resist finishing the last field.

Now, at 27 percent, wheat does not come rattling out of the combine and into the cart. It churns out noiselessly and forms a slightly tacky mess, a bit like porridge, in the cart. Instead of spreading out and finding a gentle angle of repose, the grain forms a peaked mountain in the middle of the cart, without filling out to the sides. As we surveyed our last load standing proud of the cart, rather like a Whippy ice cream, the contractor of few words said, without a hint of a smile, "Have ye a rope to tie her on?"

I enjoyed that. It reminded me of the old harvests when we were not each shut up in our machines, and repartee was an important part of the work. Like when the first loads of sheaves were seen going from the fields across the river up to the corn yard at Wardford, somebody would shout, "I see the craws are nestin' again at Wardies."

The only blot on my landscape is that the banker is looking happy. He has been smiling at me and that makes me nervous.

The Irishman gives us some tips

IT ISN'T often that I have something really useful to tell you, but that I have today. And this tip, on how to take the expense and backache out of even more of farming, comes from a source that some may think surprising. For the man who has so enlightened us is the Irishman who bought Mossie's out-farm.

Having lifted all our valuations and so improved our balance sheets, the Irishman was always bound to be popular in Aberdeenshire, but if he comes up with more tips like this, he'll be a real Godsend. He has imported an idea which can revolutionise the making of slurry pits.

Our way has always been to get in a JCB and take out a hole big enough to house at least four pits of the required size. Then a mason is called in to build four walls down the hole and plaster them. Then three-quarters of the product of the giant hole is put back in as back-filling and a floor is laid, preferably with ready-mixed concrete. With skilled masons to pay, and cement blocks to buy, you are talking thousands for a big slurry pit.

But the Irishman is going to save us a fortune.

What they do over the water is to get the JCB with a little draining bucket to take out a rectangular drain to the required dimensions. Then the drain is filled with ready-mixed concrete. When the cement is hard, the JCB scoops out the earth and you get the ready-mix cart back to pour in enough for the floor.

Job done, and no skilled labour required. There is no back-filling to be done either, which makes the Irish slurry pit that much stronger. If it really works, we'll soon have slatted areas all over Aberdeenshire, and it will be all thanks to the Irishman.

So our new neighbour is off to a flying start and he has a sense of humour too.

Mossie was trying to get the Irishman to come to Mossside and try out the Starshoot. That toy is a sophistication of clay pigeon shooting. It con-

sists of a mass of metal pipes, maybe sixty feet high, in the shape of half a dartboard. The clays come firing out of the bullseye, and you score according to where on the dartboard you shoot them.

Mossie bought the Starshoot at a bankrupt sale and intends to get it fitted to an old articulated lorry, and operated by a series of rams, so that he can tour the shows with it.

Anyway, he'd been trying to get the Irishman to come and try starshooting when he was rebuffed: "I would never take a gun in my hand".

Woops! There was an awkward pause round the fire at the Salmon Inn, where the Irishman was being introduced to

the discussion group. It is all right for us who have lived all our lives in a place where guns have not been fired in anger since 1745 to joke about shooting, but what about a man from Ulster?

And then the Irishman, with a menacing half turn towards Mossie, broke the ice with, "I don't think I could trust myself."

Anyway, one way or another, the guns will be busy this autumn. There is such a lot of game about. We have a covey of ten partridges which I can see from my desk as they scurry furtively about. I don't know if I should call it a covey, but there is a family of nine little pheasants (no adults) in the

Barn park which is at the other side of the steading. When we were harvesting we could often count twenty or more pheasants in the field.

There seems to be a further recovery in the numbers of brown hares and there are loads of roe deer about. But it is to the ducks that the lads are looking for the big increase in what passes for 'sport'. There is not only Penny Washer's newly dredged mill dam. Mossie has created a great new lake on one of his farms.

But it is not just that there is more water about. We have discovered a whole new feed source for the game. We call it "cuffins" and it can be had for nothing from the big grain stores.

Cuffins, which I think are plural, are what the cleaning process separates from the grain when it enters the store. There are millions of weed seeds (not among Mossie's cuffins but there are plenty in most people's). There is chaff. There are awns, light grains, and a surprising number of heavy ones too.

So, when we have been delivering our crop to Aberdeen Grain, we've been taking a return load of cuffins and leaving them handy for the game.

Now, Mossie had no ducks and then three ducks on his new lake until he dumped a load of cuffins. Then it was ten, thirty, sixty and now eighty ducks on the pond in the mornings and he can hardly keep up the supply of cuffins. In fact he's thinking of putting in an electric fence for a feed barrier to limit the uptake.

I too have been hauling home the cuffins but I'm afraid I haven't been so successful with the ducks. You see, we were in a hurry to get the cart filled again when the first load came home, so we dumped it for the pheasants in a rough bit of the Piggery park.

The pheasants didn't get a chance. My hill cows were tidying the Piggery park after the combine and they ate the cuffins clean. And they've devoured four more loads since. Now there is some good scratching left, and the next load goes into the mill dam for the ducks.

October 10, 1994

No more dough from the Breadwinner

I MUST have been sounding too smug - carried away with the sheen on my calves, my easy harvest, and the fact that all my next spring's work was done by the end of September. Or maybe it is just one of those things sent as a test by a Maker who is still unsure of us. Perhaps it is just Sod's Law. But disaster has struck.

The Breadwinner has decided to cash in her baking tray, hang up her rolling pin and come home and look after me. She has retired.

Of course, like any other with any care for the quiet life, or who has studied what modern marital law can do to a farm business, the Farmer loves his Breadwinner, but having her at home all the time may not be an unmitigated blessing.

I don't want to labour the point, but let me give you one example of how the Farmer's life will change. He can kiss goodbye to those jolly working lunches down with the boys at the Salmon, and then home for a quick couple of hours in the hammock.

But that is not what is worrying me. It is the sheer waste of this decision to retire. The Breadwinner is so good at winning bread, it seems a shame to give it up just to keep me in order.

I have always believed that a good working wife is the most important machine on a farm. That has been absolutely essential in the difficult era since they abandoned 'Food From our Own Resources'. But you can't put a banker's daughter between the shafts of a barrow (unless it's for a photograph) and, like any other toonser, she's absolutely hopeless as a gate. (Isn't it amazing how they always leave just enough room at one side for the cows to slip past them?)

She did try doing the books in the early days, but that was a very poor success. She just couldn't get the hang of farm books. As a banker's daughter, she was used to money being

216

earned - and then invested. She just couldn't handle borrowing and then spending, let alone spending, and then going to see if the banker would lend.

And she was quite confused by the way the residual, which in all the classes to which she went was called 'profit', in the case of the farm books turned out to be negative and was called 'loss'. When the Breadwinner was on for book-keeper she couldn't handle the bank at all. She just couldn't see that when you put money into our account, the balance always went down.

The Breadwinner never quite got to grips with the Little Ardo credit control and response system either. That was taught me by a pal who now farms in New Zealand.

There, you have to go to the post office for your mail as there is no delivery service - nae posties.

My friend used to collect once a week, and open it all beside the wastepaper basket in the post office. His aim was to leave as much as possible in that wastepaper basket. He took home only what was of interest to him, and in his interest. That included very little, and certainly did not include any bills which were not yet at the point of threatening legal action.

Because of that system of paper-control, Johnny needed only a very small filing cabinet - and I thought it a very suitable way to proceed.

The Breadwinner did not agree. She was appalled to see all those bills going straight into the bin, along with the delivery notes and advertising bumff. What really finished her was when she accepted that she would never get me to stop filing some of the red bills down behind the back seat in my car.

She resigned from that job and concentrated on highly-rewarded employment in the toon. It was a capital move from the point of view of the Farmer. It meant he could concentrate on growing grain and potatoes and breeding cattle, unencumbered by any need to be efficient with the paper.

Indeed, it is just possible that the Farmer may have had it too easy, and that that may have led to trouble. You see, the Breadwinner, though dissociating herself from the farming fiasco, did see it as her duty to see her children were fed and she could hardly feed them without feeding the Farmer. That meant that, no matter how high the overdraft went, or how unreasonable the banker became, we always knew there would be something nice for tea.

217

I was able to put up new sheds, buy expensive loss-makers from all over the continent, win championships at the Highland Show, top the market at the Perth Bull Sales, boast of my seven hundred cattle, and watch the overdraft go above £1,000 an acre. Thank goodness I didn't have more acres.

She even bought me a good second-hand slurry tanker for my birthday, and let me get on with the folly of farming.

I have a vision from our time in Africa, which encapsulates our relationship in those days. A farmer is walking along the road whistling happily and carefree. Behind him is an enormous pile of firewood, which appears to be following him under its own steam. Closer examination reveals that the farmer's wife is, of course, underneath, carrying the sticks.

So I owe her a lot, and I'm sure that life with the retired Breadwinner will still be tolerable provided I do exactly as I'm told.

But what am I to call the Breadwinner now that she is no longer winning bread?

We had a neighbour here in the forties and fifties who drank well beyond the limits of his wife's patience. He called her the Bengal Tiger. She's been dead for many years, so the name is available.

The Irishman gets Mossie into cattle

THE IRISHMAN, that most welcome incomer who took his solvency in his hands by buying Mossie's out-farm, seems to be getting on fine, despite his continuing friendship with the farmer of Moss-side. But he hasn't had the wind in his back all the way.

One of the Irishman's ideas in coming to Scotland was to get away from the troubles in Northern Ireland. Well, you can understand him doing that, and it was very understandable that he should choose Aberdeen-shire, where no one even knows what all the fuss across the Irish sea is about. We know it has something to do with religion, but we don't have a lot of that here. Catholics and Protestants we don't have. Here, it's just those who sometimes go to church, and those who hardly ever go.

I'm sure the Irishman's strategy will prove sound, but it did get off to an unbelievably unfortunate start. The very week he arrived in Scotland, the IRA announced they were to adopt an alternative way of life. And on that same week somebody, with no sense of history, or no desire to learn its lessons, planted what in more skilful hands would have been a bomb - outside the Town House in Aberdeen.

Anyway, Mossie is taking him in hand and advising the Irishman on his every move, so he'll not have his troubles to seek. Or so we all thought. But the farm is looking very well, and Mossie still hasn't got him into pigs.

In fact, we are all gobsmacked by the fact that the Irishman seems to be doing what no one in Scotland, and certainly not his saintly wife, has ever been able to achieve. The Irishman seems to be imposing his character on Mossie.

"All I know about really is *Cyattle,*" says the Irishman. But Mossie is always saying that cattle are just disasters. In his early days he nearly lost his fortune on them and, even now, he refers to cattle as "the loss adjusters."

"Cattle?" he said to me the

other day, "That's tax-evasion for you. When I had cattle I never paid a penny of tax, and I'm telling you, farming without the taxman is no fun."

Fair enough, but in that case, what was he doing down at the blacksmith's on Tuesday discussing angle barriers with the smith? And was the Irishman not away up to the big sale of cattle at Inverness on Saturday, with a big order for Mossside?

We tackled Mossie about it at the discussion group on Sunday, and all he would say was that he'd had such a good year with the cereals and the rape that he felt it would break his neighbours' hearts if he didn't find some way to get rid of a heap of cash.

But I think he's too late. He'll never lose enough money buying now. If he had bought, as so many did, a few hundred steers in the springtime he could now be setting a huge loss against his profits from the combinable crops. But at today's prices he must be in considerable danger of making even more money, come the Spring day.

Having conserved some two hundred tonnes of straw by treating it with ammonia, I'm even tempted to follow the Irishman and buy a few more cattle for the winter. Black grains and maize glutens are looking cheap I'm told, and we could easily hold another fifty young stock.

And my problems are a bit different from Mossie's. Far from needing to get rid of an embarrassment of cash, I'll have to do something if I am to preserve the profit made in this great harvest. You see, the Breadwinner's retiral has had a negative effect on the cash flow - in all sorts of unexpected ways.

Of course, I knew I would lose her salary, but that is only the start.

Now that she is retired she has time for shopping. One of the reasons why we have remained solvent is that she has never been a shopper. She always bought the groceries, of course, but she has never been one to set off, cheque book in hand, for the boutiques in case she might miss something. She hasn't really got going yet, but there are little signs. Only last week she bought a new pair of shoes although the old ones still hadn't a hole in them.

A more pressing threat to my cash flow is that she has managed to catch up with the bills. Like most farmers, I have always financed at least half my tenant's capital by making my creditors wait. But now, with all this time on her hands, the Breadwinner has got them all paid.

It's not all loss though. Those firms who have supplied us with cattle feed, manure, seeds and a new graip every ten years, have been used to waiting six months for payment, so they are always willing to give a week anyway. Two and a half percent discount for a week's credit is well over 100 percent on an annual basis so I argue I'm now getting my supplies for nothing.

And there are more savings yet.

you a bit off for cash. Up till now, I haven't been very interested because two and a half percent isn't very attractive against six months credit.

But now that I know she's going to pay on invoice, I have been astonishing the salesmen by twisting their arms for a discount if I give them the cheque away with them. They think it a bargain, but I know they'd have had their money in

On Saturday she went down to the wood my grandfather planted in 1936 and gathered brambles which, with a few of the diseased, wizened apples which is all we can grow here, were enough for an excellent tart.

Next thing she'll be darning my socks, and sewing buttons on my shirts.

This is the way forward.

221

Also available from Ardo

Green Heritage

*This novel was written in the early thirties by
John R. Allan and published posthumously in 1990. It is the
story of a successful young London business man who discovers his roots in North-east Scotland.*
Price now £9.95

A Lucky Chap

*The autobiography of Sir Maitland Mackie, who with his
father founded what became the biggest farming business in
Scotland. It recalls his upbringing on the farm at Tarves. It
also tells about his time as the Queen's representative in
Aberdeenshire and how he got on with the Royals.
It tells mostly of eighty years of fun.*
Price still £12.50

A Desert Rat
in Holburn Street

*The autobiography of an Aberdeenshire lad who joined up
in the second world war and quickly found himself in the
desert war. He drove tanks in North Africa, Italy and France,
and stayed alive when so many of his comrades died. After
the war he built up a succesful grocery business in
Holburn Street, Aberdeen.*
Price now £9.95

Farmer's Diary

*Charlie Allan farmed with very middling success from 1973,
when he quit his post of Senior Lecturer in Economics at
Strathclyde University, until 1986 when his wife Fiona took
a three-year aid job in Nairobi, Kenya. They returned to
Scotland in 1989. This diary tells how he got the farm going
again, tried to keep the banker happy and re-established a
place in the small North-east community of Methlick.
This volume covers a long year to Christmas 1990.
Illustrated by Jim Turnbull.
Price now £9.95*

Volume II

*Charlie continues his record of the never-ending battle with
the weather and beaurocracy. He recounts the fun had by
Mossie, Red Rooster and the other lads of the discussion
group which meets at the Salmon Inn on a Sunday night to
blow about their crop yields or drown their sorrows when the
weather wins. This volume covers the year 1991 and continues to the end of February 1993.
Illustrated by Jim Turnbull.
Price now £9.95*

Volume III

*Volume III covers the period from March 1992 to the end of
June 1993. Charlie is still trying to grow the 4-tonne crop.
There are marriages and births among the lads of the
discussion group; sales and purchases of farms. But the
biggest changes are brought in by the EC in the form of
set-aside, and the EC commissioner from Ireland,
Mr MacSharry, becomes the hero of Volume III.
Illustrated by Jim Turnbull.
Price £9.95*

All titles available at bookshops
throughout the North-east
or direct from Methlick
Please add £1 for postage

Ardo Publishing Company Ltd.
Methlick, Aberdeenshire AB41 0HR
Tel/Fax 01651 806218